CW00427981

# INTRODUCTION TO MICROBIOI

# Basic microbiology

EDITOR: J. F. WILKINSON

## Volume I
# Introduction to microbiology

J. F. WILKINSON M.A., PH.D.
Professor of Microbiology, University of Edinburgh

SECOND EDITION

BLACKWELL SCIENTIFIC PUBLICATIONS
OXFORD LONDON EDINBURGH
BOSTON MELBOURNE

ISBN 0 632 03170

First published 1972
Second edition 1975
Reprinted 1977, 1978, 1980

German edition 1974
Spanish edition 1976
Italian edition 1977

Distributed in the U.S.A. by
Halstead Press, a Division of
John Wiley & Sons Inc.
New York

Printed and bound in Great Britain by
Whitstable Litho Ltd.,
Whitstable, Kent

# Contents

# Preface

This book is designed to be used as an introduction to Microbiology. Although no prior knowledge of microorganisms is required, it is assumed that the reader has an elementary understanding of the basic principles of biology and, in particular, those of biochemistry and, to a lesser extent, of genetics.

The subject of microbiology is assumed to cover eukaryotic microorganisms (algae, fungi and protozoa) as well as the more commonly covered bacteria and viruses although the general principles involved are illustrated by those organisms most suited for the purpose; these organisms often happen to be bacteria and their viruses.

This volume is the first in a series of short textbooks with the following titles:

1. Introduction to Microbiology
2. Introduction to Modern Virology
3. Physiology of Microorganisms
4. Biology of Microorganisms
5. Microbial Ecology
6. Agricultural Microbiology
7. Industrial Microbiology
8. Medical Microbiology

These volumes are intended to provide together a coordinated textbook of Microbiology. At the same time, an attempt has been made to render the individual books explicable in their own right. The choice would depend on the requirements of the reader. Thus a student of Agricultural Microbiology might require only Volumes 1 and 6. In order to fulfil this purpose, some of the material has had to be duplicated of necessity, but the extent of this duplication has been reduced to a minimum.

I should like to thank the other members of the Department of Microbiology at Edinburgh University who have become involved in the series for their many suggestions. In addition I am much indebted to Gordon Finnie for drawing most of the illustrations and to Dolores Stewart for the difficult task of transcribing my writing into typescript.

# 1 Introduction

Microbiology is the study of microorganisms. This is clear enough but it is by no means so certain how microorganisms should be defined and, for the moment, we may simply say that they are a collection of the simplest forms of life which are lumped together for convenience. Microbiology was the last of the three major divisions of Biology to develop and there have been continued attempts to include all organisms under the disciplines of Botany and Zoology. Thus bacteria, algae and fungi have been considered to be part of the Plant Kingdom while protozoa have been included in the Animal Kingdom. Unfortunately, this has meant that microorganisms were generally ignored since specialised techniques were required for their study. The main stimulus to the development of microbiology as a separate science was the discovery that they caused disease. Departments studying microorganisms and, in particular, bacteria, were set up in medical schools. It is only much more recently that non-medical microbiology departments have been formed, a situation partly catalysed by the use of microorganisms in the study of basic biological principles and especially those of Molecular Biology.

It is now usual to include five major groups as microorganisms leading to subsequent subdivision of microbiology into virology, bacteriology, phycology, mycology and protozoology, i.e.

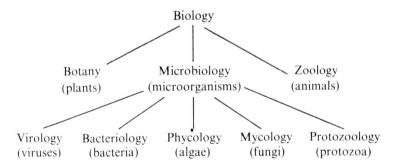

What is the justification for the separation of microbiology as a distinct discipline? There are probably three main reasons which will become clearer later. The first is that the majority of organisms making up the major microbial groups are of microscopic dimensions. Some are, or can be, multicellular but if they are, there is generally no differentiation into tissues as in higher organisms. The second and perhaps the most important, is that the techniques used to study microorganisms are similar for all groups and generally different from those used for plants and animals. The third is that microorganisms often form an interrelated group in nature. These are some of the reasons for considering microbiology as a separate science and although in theory the ideal way to organise research into biology is no doubt as a single discipline with a shifting series of internal boundaries as the subject develops, in practice some subdivision is necessary for practical purposes and it is likely that microbiology would inevitably evolve as a separate discipline.

A subject can only develop according to the techniques available. This may sound platitudinous but any study of the history of microbiology will demonstrate the prime importance of suitable methodology. Three techniques in particular had to be perfected before the science of microbiology could evolve beyond a primitive visionary state.

(1) *Microscopy*. Since microbiology is mainly concerned with the study of living organisms of microscopic dimensions, its development depended for its initiation entirely upon the refinement of the microscope.

(2) *Sterilisation methods*. Media to be used for growth of a particular microorganism had to be freed from all other living organisms; in other words sterilisation methods had to be developed.

(3) *Pure culture methods*. Once it was possible to obtain sterile growth media, it became practicable to introduce methods to separate different microorganisms from each other and to maintain them in pure culture. Their individual characteristics could then be studied. Let us consider each of these critical developments in turn.

## THE MICROSCOPE

Prior to the seventeenth century, there had been various reports of the existence of invisible living creatures but, before the development of suitable means of magnifying them, no proof was obtainable. To Anthonie van Leeuwenhoek, a merchant and amateur scientist living in Delft, belongs the honour of providing the first accurate report of the occurrence of bacteria. Leeuwenhoek employed his spare time in pursuing his hobby of making lenses which he used to build magnifying glasses of high resolving power. These single-lens microscopes were of the simplest possible design (see Fig. 1.1), but were still capable of magnifying an object by about 200-fold. As a result of his exceptionally painstaking care in

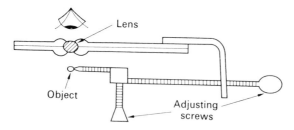

**Figure 1.1** The type of microscope used by Leeuwenhoek. The object is placed at the end of a wire attached to a screw and is viewed through the small lens

the building and use of his microscopes, Leeuwenhoek was able to make descriptions of many microorganisms including some which were almost certainly bacteria. Anybody who has tried to use a reproduction of one of his instruments will soon realise that his particular genius fulfils the criterion of an infinite capacity to take pains. Using a racy style that would nowadays be the subject of multitudinous editorial transformation, he communicated the results of his work in the form of letters to the recently founded Royal Society of London. An example is given in this excerpt of a letter of 1684 in which those organisms described as E (Fig. 1.2) probably represents the first description of bacteria.

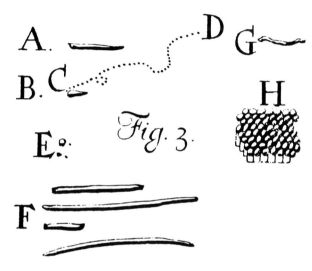

Figure 1.2 Leeuwenhoek's famous drawing of micro-organisms published in 1684. Different shaped organisms can be seen, some of which were almost certainly bacteria

'Though my teeth are kept usually very clean, nevertheless when I view them in a magnifying glass, I find growing between them a little white matter.... I took some of this flower and mixed it with pure rain water wherein were no animals ... and to my great surprise perceived that the aforesaid matter contained many small living animals, which moved themselves very extravagantly. The biggest sort had the shape of A, their motion was strong and nimble, and they darted themselves thro the water as a Jack or Pike does through water.... The second sort had the shape of B. These spun about like a Top.... In the third sort I could not well distinguish the figure, for sometimes it seemed to be an oval and other times a circle. These were so small that they seem'd no bigger than E.'

These observations of Leeuwenhoek were followed by a period of nearly two centuries during which there was little further descriptive work on the smaller microorganisms because nobody was capable of designing a microscope which had a sufficient resolving power but which could, at the same time, be used by a worker of average dexterity and patience. Further progress depended upon the development of a compound microscope with an eyepiece and objective lens allowing an increase in the magnification obtainable and greater ease of manipulation. It is true that people like Robert Hooke had used compound microscopes in the seventeenth century but they were incapable of the performance given by Leeuwenhoek's single-lens microscopes. The reason for this lay in defects such as chromatic and spherical aberration inherent in their basic design. During the eighteenth century these defects were gradually overcome by the following refinements:

(1) Corrected complex eyepiece and objective lenses.

(2) A condenser to focus light on the object.

(3) A thin glass coverslip to place over a liquid drop on a glass slide so that objects within the liquid could be viewed in a flat plane.

(4) The oil-immersion lens. The resolving power of a microscope can be increased by using a material between the objective lens of higher refractility than air. The material most commonly used is a special immersion oil.

In conjunction with these developments in microscopic design, staining methods were perfected so as to allow a simple classification of microorganisms based on morphological grounds. However, the theoretical limit of resolution of the light microscope is about 0·2 $\mu$m and clearly gives little hope of seeing much internal structural detail in a typical bacterium of 0·5–1·0 $\mu$m diameter. The only way to increase the magnification was either to increase the numerical aperture of the microscope which was difficult in practice or to decrease the wavelength of the light used. Ultraviolet light can give, because of its short wavelength, a resolution of about 0·1 $\mu$m but requires quartz lenses and a camera or a fluorescent screen to see the magnified object; in consequence the ultraviolet microscope has been used mainly to show structures which have special properties under ultraviolet light (e.g. specific absorption of fluorescence). Just as there was a quiescent period for microbial cytology between the work of Leeuwenhoek and the sophistication of the compound microscope, so there was little real progress between the latter half of the nineteenth century and the development of the electron microscope in the 1940's. The small wavelength of an electron beam allows a theoretical resolving power down to 0·01 nm or 0·001Å and for the first time, viruses could be demonstrated as physical entities. Practical difficulties in instrument design such as the development of magnetic lenses have prevented resolutions as low as this but it is still possible to see the larger molecules that make up the architecture of a cell. In practice only thin objects can be viewed with any real hope of obtaining good definition of internal structures and so methods had to be developed in which cells are fixed, dehydrated, embedded in plastic and sectioned to give a preparation about 100 nm thick (i.e. about 10 to a bacterial cell). Some increase in contrast can be obtained by using electron-dense stains like osmic acid, permanganate, or uranium salts. Another problem in electron microscopy is the possibility of artefacts caused by fixation, drying and embedding; this difficulty can be partly obviated by the use of freeze-etching in which a carbon replica is made of a frozen surface in a cell (Fig. 2.8, p. 28). In spite of the many difficulties involved

4

in its use and, particularly, in the interpretation of results, the electron microscope has opened up a new world to microbial cytologists.

## METHODS OF STERILISATION

Sterilisation involves the complete destruction or removal of all living organisms from the object being sterilised. The development of methods for sterilisation was very largely a happy consequence of the controversy over spontaneous generation culminating in the work of Pasteur. Although the spontaneous generation of mice from old rags and of maggots from meat had been disproved in the seventeenth century, the idea that the microorganisms shown by Leeuwenhoek were produced *de novo* was still popular in the first half of the nineteenth century. It was known that the fermentation of fruit juices was associated with the production of large microorganisms (yeasts) and of alcohol and $CO_2$; the putrefaction of animal or plant extracts and the souring of milk paralleled the growth of smaller microorganisms (bacteria) and the accumulation of lactic acid and foul-smelling chemicals such as amines. What caused what? Did fermentation cause the spontaneous production of yeasts or did yeasts bring about fermentation? The answer may seem obvious today but in those days it was not and it is fascinating to read the early experiments to prove or disprove spontaneous generation and to experience the righteousness of wrong-headedness. To do so makes one a little less arrogant about the present state of science; some of our dogma may be based on equally wrong premises.

Experiments designed to prove or to disprove spontaneous generation depended upon two general principles.

(a) The complete sterilisation of a suitable growth medium so that no living organisms exist at the start of the experiment.

(b) The design of the vessel so that it is impossible for microorganisms to enter from the outside. This was necessary following the realisation of the existence of microorganisms floating around in the air. For example, even 'fresh' air may contain one particle carrying a microorganism per cubic foot while the figure may be a hundred to a thousand times greater in a crowded room.

Provided these principles are rigidly adhered to and provided the conditions are otherwise suitable for microbial multiplication, any growth occurring must be the result of spontaneous generation. Clearly the key question was how good were the methods for attaining and maintaining sterility and such was the emotional fervour aroused by a controversy which involved the very nature of life that many important scientists became involved. The technical 'fall-out' was the development of sterilisation methods. Let us consider the two principles in greater detail.

(1) *The attainment of sterility.* The usual method depended upon heat treatment, which was known to be inimical to most forms of life. However, it was soon realised that microorganisms vary widely in their resistance to heating (Fig. 1.4) and sterilisation clearly must be gauged to the most resistant forms.

5

In general, bacteria required higher temperatures than larger forms and some microorganisms can produce specialised heat-stable structures called spores (p. 20). Boiling at normal pressures was insufficient to kill these spores and so autoclaves were designed to increase the pressure and, thereby, the temperature.

(2) *The maintenance of sterility.* In experiments claiming to show spontaneous generation, a cork was often used to prevent the entry of contaminants from outside. Unfortunately this method was ineffective in practice since microorganisms could enter round the side of the cork as the vessels cooled after sterilisation. Although a flask could be hermetically sealed, this led to the objection that oxygen, a substance known to be essential for many forms of life, could no longer enter the vessel. It was necessary, therefore, to include some sort of filter to prevent the entry of microorganisms but not of air. This led to the development of the cotton-wool plug which was soon adopted universally by microbiologists. However, one of the simplest and most elegant means of preventing the entry of microorganisms can be seen in Pasteur's swan-necked flask (see Fig. 1.3) which depended upon the fact that organisms in the atmosphere entering the open end of the tube would, in their slow passage through

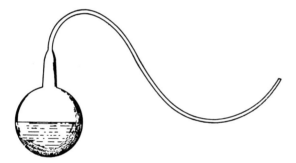

**Figure 1.3** The swan-necked flask used by Pasteur to demonstrate the absence of spontaneous generation

the convolutions, be deposited by the pull of gravity. Pasteur showed that such flasks, although left open, remained sterile indefinitely. By such simple means, he finally disproved the idea of spontaneous generation, a result aided by his skill as an expositor of his own work and by an almost evangelical zeal.

However, although the brilliance and the force of Pasteur's personality were able to catalyse the early adolescence of microbiology, he later acted as an inhibitor of progress since it was often felt that 'surely Pasteur can't be wrong'. For example, he firmly believed that metabolic processes such as fermentation were an essential property of the 'living force' and could not occur in the absence of living cells and for a long time this view was generally held. In science as elsewhere an inhibition of progress is the price we may have to pay for an innovating genius.

By the end of the nineteenth century most of the methods currently used for sterilisation had been developed and are briefly summarised below.

## Heat

If the percentage of survivors of a microorganism is plotted against time a logarithmic relationship is found. The slope of the line varies from organism to organism but in the choice of a general sterilisation method we must use a time and temperature that will kill all organisms including heat-resistant spores. This is illustrated in Fig. 1.4, where it can be seen that if a time of 30 minutes is used for sterilisation, microorganism A will require a temperature of only 50° while B needs 60–70° and the bacterial spore suspension C, 120°. The methods generally adopted are as follows.

(a) *Wet heat in an autoclave.* The usual method is a time of 30 minutes at a pressure of 1·05 kg/cm² (15 lb/sq in), which will give a temperature of 121°. This is the best method if it is practicable.

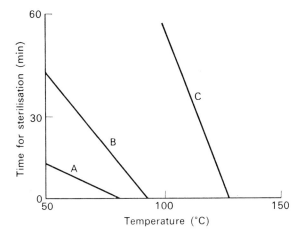

**Figure 1.4** The death curves resulting from heat treatment of two suspensions of vegetative cells of microorganisms A and B and a spore suspension from microorganism C

(b) *Tyndallisation.* A course of three periods of boiling at 100° for 30 minutes at daily intervals. The spores remaining at the end of the first stage will germinate as the temperature is lowered; this results in a loss of heat-resistance so that the vegetative cells are killed at the second or third boiling. This process is occasionally used for materials such as sugar media likely to be affected by the higher temperatures used in an autoclave.

(c) *Dry heat.* Water acts as a catalyst in the killing of microorganisms by heat and in its absence, as in a dry oven, a temperature of 160° for 2 hours is usually required.

(d) *Pasteurisation.* This is not a method of sterilisation since it involves treating for an insufficient time for complete killing, e.g. to about 60° for 30 minutes; this treatment will kill most disease-producing bacteria present in natural products such as milk without affecting the flavour or consistency.

## Filtration

The liquid or gas to be sterilised is passed through a filter with a porosity sufficient to remove any microorganisms in suspension. The use of cotton wool for gases has already been mentioned and for liquids a variety of filters are available made of materials such as asbestos (Seitz filters) or cellulose nitrate (Millipore filters). Filtration is obviously the method of choice for the sterilisation of liquids containing heat-labile components.

## Radiation

Certain regions of the radiation spectrum are lethal to microorganisms. Ultraviolet light is especially effective and is valuable in sterilising air. However, it penetrates poorly and for the interior of solid objects it is necessary to use ionising radiations from a source such as radioactive cobalt.

## Chemicals

Many chemicals are lethal to microorganisms in general but they may require a long and impracticable exposure for complete sterilisation and are often difficult to remove subsequently. Hypochlorite solutions and phenolic derivatives are used as general laboratory disinfectants as is gaseous ethylene oxide for more specialised purposes. However, it must be realised that the chemicals often used as disinfectants rarely cause sterilisation under the conditions employed.

## PURE CULTURE METHODS

As soon as microbial growth media could be sterilised effectively it became theoretically possible to isolate pure cultures. However, although Pasteur had shown that different fermentation and putrefaction processes were associated with the growth of morphologically different microbes (e.g. yeast with alcohol fermentation, a variety of shapes of bacteria with lactic, acetic and butyric fermentations), some scientists held that all microorganisms, and particularly all bacteria, were variants of a single basic type—the concept of *pleomorphism*. Others believed in *monomorphism*—that is in a large number of different organisms which should all be obtainable in pure culture. Could they? Ultimately any method must depend upon the introduction of a *single* microbial cell into a sterile growth medium in a suitable vessel. Unfortunately, the small size of most microorganisms made mechanical separation of single cells impossible. It is true that the more recent development of the micromanipulator has made this feat possible, but it is a difficult and specialised instrument for general use. Instead other methods had to be discovered which had the effect of diluting a sample so that single cells were obtained which could grow to produce a pure culture. The first methods depended upon a dilution of the culture until an aliquot was likely to contain a single cell as judged from an initial count. However, such methods are tedious, unreliable and can only be employed for the dominant organism. They are now rarely used and instead microbiologists began to study the possibility of diluting on a solid surface. The sample is placed at one point on a sterile solid growth medium and then, using a sterile needle, the sample, or *inoculum* as it is called, is drawn several times over the surface. Each streak represents a dilution process and eventually single cells are obtained along the streak each of which, on incubation, grow up into a separate colony which can be used as the source of a pure culture. This *streak method* for the isolation of pure cultures was pioneered by Robert Koch who realised that the most effective surface to use was a solidified form of a normal growth medium. At first he employed gelatin as a solidifying agent but it suffered from liquefying at temperatures above 28° and, being a protein, it can be hydrolysed by some microorganisms. A nearly ideal substance was found in the poly-saccharide agar-agar (usually called simply agar) occurring in some seaweeds;

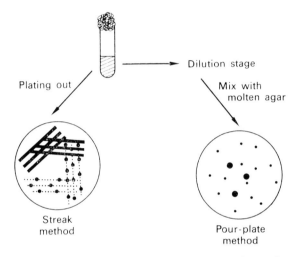

Dilution stage

Plating out

Mix with molten agar

Streak method

Pour-plate method

**Figure 1.5** Methods for obtaining a pure culture of a microorganism. The original liquid culture in the example contains two organisms, one producing large colonies and the other producing small colonies

an agar gel melts at about 100° and will not solidify again until the temperature falls to about 40°. Furthermore agar is attacked by very few microorganisms. Its unique properties allowed an alternative to the streak method—the *pour-plate* method. A diluted sample of the microorganism is mixed with a previously-melted agar growth medium at a temperature just above the solidifying point. The mixture is poured into a suitable vessel and is incubated. Each cell produces a colony within the agar.

Using such pure-culture methods, Koch and others were able to associate particular diseases with particular microorganisms. The techniques were then applied to the whole range of microbes occurring in natural environments. However, if a nutrient medium suitable for the growth of most microorganisms is employed, only the predominant organisms are likely to be isolated. Take, for

9

example, the microorganisms inhabiting our mouths; a typical sample may contain the following groups of organisms in numbers per ml of saliva: yeasts, 100; lactobacilli, $2 \times 10^4$; staphylococci, $5 \times 10^5$; diphtheroids, $3 \times 10^6$; streptococci, $5 \times 10^7$; anaerobic micrococci, $5 \times 10^7$; anaerobic diplococci, $1 \times 10^8$. If we are to isolate some of the rarer organisms in pure culture we must choose environmental conditions which favour the growth of the organism we require compared with that of those we do not. This is done either by a previous *enrichment stage*, or by choosing appropriate media and conditions for the dilution and growth stage. Let us consider some of the selection methods used in practice:

(a) Growth at a high temperature (e.g. 50°) above the maximum for most microorganisms will select for 'heat-loving' or thermophilic species (see p. 54). Alternatively, if this sample is pasteurised (p. 7) before growth, sporing species will in general be isolated.

(b) Growth in the absence of a source of nitrogen in the growth medium but in presence of air will select those organisms capable of utilising atmospheric nitrogen—the nitrogen-fixing microorganisms (p. 70).

(c) Growth in the absence of oxygen will select those organisms capable of anaerobic growth (p. 55).

(d) Microorganisms growing in mammalian intestines have to be able to withstand the presence of bile salts which inhibit the growth of most other microbes. If a medium is made up containing suitable nutrients together with bile salts, intestinal bacteria are favoured; this property is the basis of methods used for testing water supplies for faecal contamination (p. 93).

These are a few examples of the environmental conditions that can be devised to increase the percentage of the desired microorganism from a mixed inoculum so that single colonies can be isolated. Using these and similar methods, microbiologists were able to show the vast range of microorganisms occurring in nature. The science of microbiology had come of age.

# 2 The structure of microorganisms

The introduction of the light microscope allowed microbiologists to determine the over-all shape of cells and, in the case of multicellular organisms, their arrangement. Furthermore some internal structure can be seen by the use of the phase-contrast microscope or by staining methods. Most of the stains used, such as basic dyes, were relatively non-specific and gave little idea of the chemical nature or function of a cellular component while others were more specific; fat-soluble dyes such as Sudan Black stained lipid granules and iodine showed up starch granules. However, in smaller microorganisms such as bacteria, the size of the cell (say about 0·5 $\mu$m in diameter) was only slightly greater than the theoretical limit of resolution of the light microscope (about 0·2 $\mu$m). The study of the ultrastructure of cells depended on the introduction of the electron microscope although we have already mentioned that the occurrence of artefacts produced in the preparation of specimens cannot be ruled out. Furthermore, as in all cytological investigations, it is very easy to see what one is looking for by selection of appropriate microscopic fields. Consider the well-known poem of Hilaire Belloc:

> The microbe is so very small
> You cannot make him out at all,
> But many sanguine people hope
> To see him through a microscope.
> His jointed tongue that lies beneath
> A hundred curious rows of teeth,
> His seven tufted tails with lots
> Of lovely pink and purple spots
> On each of which a pattern stands
> Composed of forty separate bands;
> His eyebrows of a tender green
> All these have never yet been seen
> But scientists who ought to know
> Assure us that they must be so.
> *Oh, let us never, never doubt*
> *What nobody is sure about*

Although Belloc's visions leave something to be desired as an exposition of microbial structure, the final 'punch' lines are particularly appropriate to the cytologist who needs considerable integrity and perhaps not too much imagination.

One of the main problems in electron microscopy is in the interpretation of the chemical nature and function of the structures seen. Unfortunately there are essentially very few *specific* stains available and although there may be potentialities in the use of specific antibodies labelled with an electron dense component like ferritin, technical difficulties have prevented their common use. Consequently the primary method used for relating structure to function is to break open the cell and to fractionate the components which are then subject to biochemical analysis. Another problem is the difficulty of rupturing a cell without denaturing the more sensitive components, particularly in bacteria with their small size

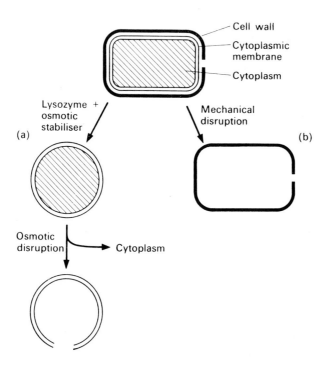

**Figure 2.1** Two methods for bacterial disruption. (a) Involves treatment with lysozyme in presence of an osmotic stabiliser followed by a controlled osmotic lysis. (b) Involves mechanical disruption with glass beads

and tough walls. However, methods of breakdown have been gradually developed and most of the major cell structures can be isolated in a reasonably pure state in which they perform their functions normally. Consider two examples of cell breakage in bacteria (Fig. 2.1).

(1) Violent shaking of a bacterial suspension with glass beads causes rupture of the cell wall and liberation of the cytoplasmic contents. The walls can be concentrated by centrifugation and treated with appropriate solvents and enzymes to remove contaminating components. The walls isolated in this way

retain the shape of the original cell and are metabolically inert. They can also be completely solubilised in a few bacterial species by the enzyme lysozyme, a component of numerous animal secretions and fluids (see p. 17).

(2) Exposure of a sensitive bacterial species to lysozyme normally causes complete cell lysis. However, if the treatment is done in the presence of an osmotic stabiliser such as an isotonic sucrose solution, the cell assumes a spherical shape as the wall is solubilised. The product is called a *protoplast* and electron microscopy of thin sections shows that it is bounded by a structure called the cytoplasmic membrane. This simple experiment suggests the following:

(a) The wall determines cell shape since the protoplast is spherical irrespective of the original shape.

(b) The wall is responsible for the mechanical strength of the bacterial cell since a protoplast is very prone to mechanical or osmotic lysis while the cell is not.

(c) The cytoplasmic membrane and not the cell wall is responsible for the semi-permeable properties of the cell surface which remain unchanged in a protoplast.

(d) The cell wall is metabolically inert, the protoplast retaining the enzyme systems of the cell and being even capable of growth.

If a protoplast is subject to controlled osmotic lysis by a gradual reduction in the external osmotic pressure, the cytoplasmic membrane ruptures liberating the cytoplasm and its contents. Differential centrifugation can then be used to isolate the membranes and components of the cytoplasm which should be unaffected by the mild lytic procedure.

Using methods similar to those outlined above, the structure and function of the components of a few apparently typical cells have been obtained. It has become clear quite recently that there are two basic types of cells—prokaryotic or eukaryotic. *Prokaryotic cells* are restricted to microorganisms (bacteria, blue-green algae etc.) while *eukaryotic cells* occur in microorganisms (fungi, protozoa, and algae other than blue-green) and in animals and plants. In addition there are the viruses which have a much simpler non-cellular structure and will be dealt with at the end of this chapter. The prokaryotic cell will be considered first.

## THE PROKARYOTIC CELL

The components of a prokaryotic cell are shown in Fig. 2.2; those which occur in almost all organisms are drawn with continuous lines while those whose presence is variable depending upon the organism being studied and the cultural conditions being employed are drawn with dotted lines. The appearance of typical prokaryotic cells in thin section is shown in Plate 2.1, facing p. 16.

### Size

Although prokaryotic cells can vary in size from a *Mycoplasma* (a sphere of

13

about 0·12 $\mu$m diameter) to a blue-green algae like *Oscillatoria* (a rod of dimensions as much as 40 × 5 $\mu$m), the majority have a diameter in the region of 1 $\mu$m.

## The cytoplasmic (cell) membrane

The cytoplasmic membrane is the bounding layer of the prokaryotic protoplast. In thin sections it can be seen as a triple-layered structure consisting of two electron-dense regions surrounding an electron-transparent one (Plate 2.1, facing p. 16), a type of structure typical of all semi-permeable membranes in living organisms and called a 'unit membrane'. The chemical components of

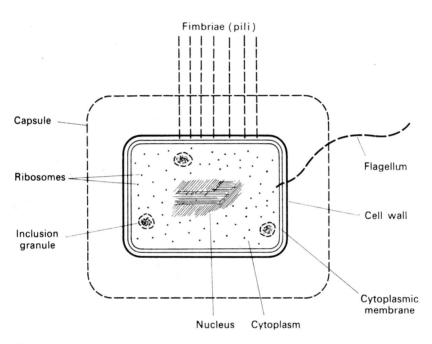

**Figure 2.2** A representation of a typical prokaryotic cell. Structures whose presence is variable are marked in dotted lines

the cytoplasmic membrane have been analysed using preparations made after controlled osmotic lysis of protoplasts (see pp. 13–14). The main components are lipid and protein present in roughly equal amounts and probably related to a triplex structure with two protein layers surrounding a lipid layer or, more likely, a loosely-bound bimolecular lipid structure with protein combined sometimes on the inner surface, sometimes on the outer surface and sometimes penetrating the membrane. However, some people believe that this structure is an artefact brought about by the fixation processes. The proteins of the membrane are similar to those of the cytoplasm in terms of amino-acid composition, while the lipids (usually phospholipids) are more characteristic and

14

vary from organism to organism. However, in distinction to eukaryotic membranes, sterols are not usually present.

The prokaryotic membrane can have the following functions:

(a) *Semi-permeable layer.* The function of allowing the entry and exit of some molecules but not others is exceedingly important and if this barrier is broken down, essential metabolites pass out of the cell and the result is death. The transport of molecules across the membrane in either direction usually involves their specific combination with protein molecules called permeases which are built into the membrane structure. Because of the specificity of this combination, a large number of different permeases may be required in any one cell. Energy provided by metabolism may be necessary for the transport process and considerable concentration within the cytoplasm compared with the external environment may occur.

(b) *Energy production.* The membrane is the site of phosphorylation reactions leading to the conversion of ADP to ATP and the membrane is therefore the site of the enzymes and carriers involved in these reactions. Further details are given in Chapter 5.

(c) *Extracellular polymer production.* The final stages in the synthesis of some of the polymers in the cell wall, capsule and extracellular fluids are catalysed by membrane enzymes. However, extracellular proteins including those in flagella and pili are assumed to be formed in ribosomes and to be specifically transported to the exterior of the cell.

(d) *Site of chromosome attachment.* (See p. 16.)

In this discussion, it has been assumed that the cytoplasmic membrane is a simple structure underlying the cell wall and following its contours. However, some infolding may occur which can produce complex structures of three

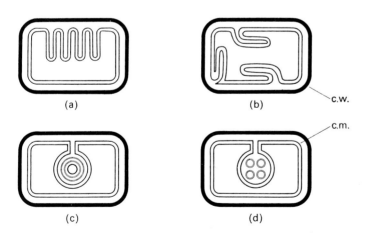

(a)    (b)    c.w.

c.m.

(c)    (d)

**Figure 2.3** Types of infoldings of the cytoplasmic membrane found in prokaryotic cells. c.m., cytoplasmic membrane; c.w., cell wall

general types: (i) Infoldings in the form of parallel plates (Fig. 2.3a), (ii) Infoldings in the form of tubes (Fig. 2.3b). Both these types effectively increase the surface area of the cell, (iii) Mesosomes (Figs. 2.2., 2.3c and d). The latter are more specialised structures although they too probably retain some degree of continuity with the cytoplasmic membrane. Their function is still obscure but may involve a role in chromosome attachment and separation (see below) or in cross-wall production (see Fig. 2.3). They are fairly common in a wide variety of bacteria but their occurrence is by no means universal.

## Cytoplasm

Within the cytoplasmic membrane occurs the cytoplasm. It contains a variety of enzymes, coenzymes and metabolites and its main function is in intermediary metabolism and in the transport of molecules from one part of a cell to another.

## The Nucleus

It is possible to use nuclear stains to delineate a central staining region provided care is taken to remove the cytoplasmic RNA which would otherwise mask the nuclear region. However, little internal structure can be seen in the nucleus and, in spite of some acrimonious debate, no mitotic process can be shown to occur. In the electron microscope, the nucleus shows as a diffuse area containing fibrous material with no limiting membrane. Because of the difference to the classical eukaryotic nucleus a variety of names have been given to this region (nuclear body, nucleoid, etc.) but in view of the identity of the basic structural and functional component (DNA) it seems better to call it simply the pro-karyotic nucleus.

Unfortunately the absence of a nuclear membrane has prevented the easy purification of isolated nuclei and if the cell is broken the nucleus disintegrates liberating a single circular chromosome thread of double-stranded DNA usually in the region of 1–2 mm (1,000–2,000 μm) in length. Since this is about a thousand times longer than the cell itself, the thread must be highly folded in the nucleus to give the bundles of fibres seen in thin sections. Although a single chromosome has only been demonstrated in a few bacteria, genetic evidence of the presence of a single linkage group in other organisms suggests a probable universal occurrence in prokaryotes. Given a single chromosome, it is not necessary to have a complex mitotic system nor a nuclear membrane. Instead, there is probably an attachment between a specific point on the chromosome and the cytoplasmic membrane (or mesosome). The first stage in nuclear division may involve duplication of this attachment site, followed by a progressive division of the DNA thread. The two nuclei are then drawn apart by separation of these attachment points.

The charges on the DNA molecule of prokaryotes do not appear to be neutralised by basic proteins as in eukaryotes and the fibres are held apart in a relatively non-condensed state, presumably to allow intermediates and essential enzymes to enter and RNA to pass out.

16

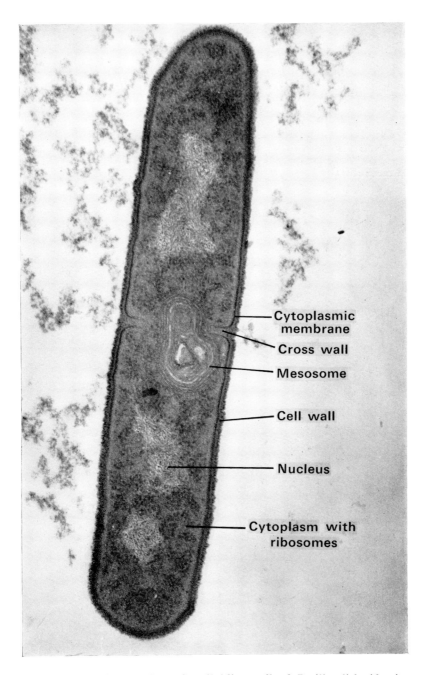

- Cytoplasmic membrane
- Cross wall
- Mesosome
- Cell wall
- Nucleus
- Cytoplasm with ribosomes

**Plate 2.1** A thin section of a dividing cell of *Bacillus licheniformis*. The mesosome is apparently involved in cross-wall formation. (Courtesy of P. Highton.) ×42,000

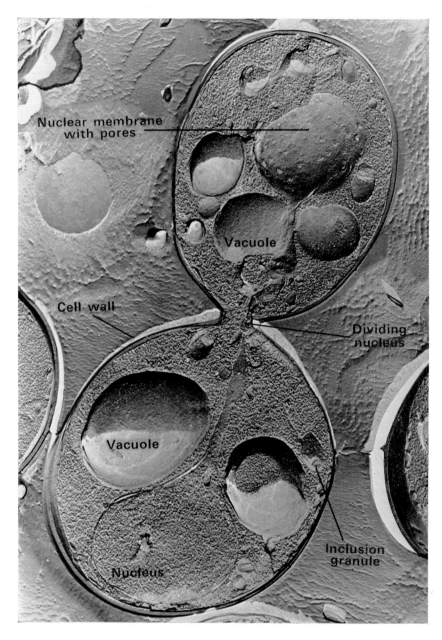

**Plate 2.2** A freeze etched preparation of the yeast *Saccharomyces cerevisiae*. The nucleus is seen dividing with a connection between the separated nuclei. (Courtesy of H. Moor.) × 15,000

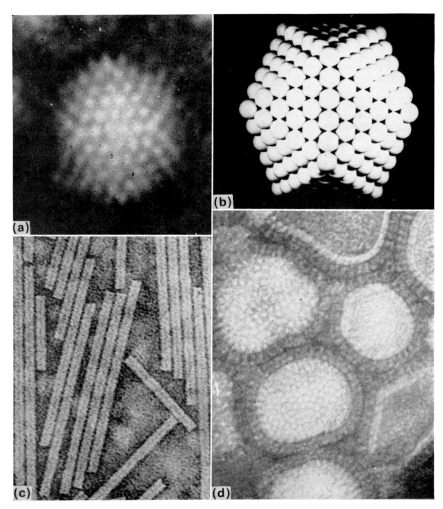

**Plate 2.3**  Different types of virus assembly. (a) and (b) Icosahedral assembly. (a) The human adenovirus (×560,000), (b) a model of the same virus showing icosahedral assembly, (c) helical assembly in tobacco mosaic virus (×144,000) in which some of the virus rods have been broken in the preparation of the specimen, and (d) enveloped virus in the human influenza virus (×320,000). All photographs by kind permission of R. W. Horne

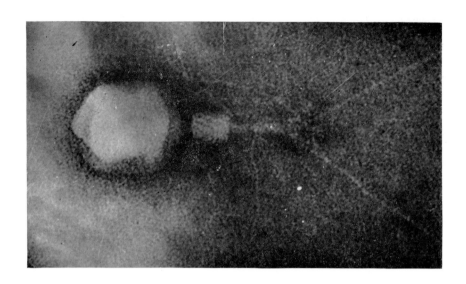

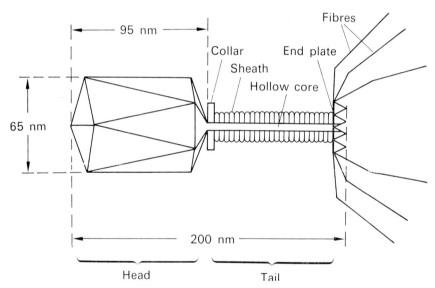

**Plate 2.4** (top) A T2 coliphage (×424,000). This virus has been triggered so that the collar is contracted (see fig. 6.3). From S. Breener *et al* (1959) *J. Mol. Biol.*, **1**, 281. (bottom) A diagrammatic representation of a T2 coliphage with the collar uncontracted

## Ribosomes

The ribosomes appear in thin sections as relatively dense particles about 20 nm in diameter. They can be easily prepared from ruptured cells by differential centrifugation on a sucrose gradient. They are made up to two sub-units of sedimentation constants 30S and 50S which combine to give the characteristic prokaryotic 70S ribosome; both components are made up of roughly equal amounts of RNA and protein. Ribosomes appear to be mainly free in the cytoplasm rather than membrane-attached as in eukaryotes, although their functional state with respect to protein synthesis is as polysomes joined by a thread of messenger RNA (m-RNA).

In general, prokaryotic cells are characterised by a considerably higher rate of multiplication than eukaryotic cells and this difference is reflected in the number of ribosomes per unit mass. In rapidly growing bacteria, they may make up about 40% of the cell dry weight.

## Storage granules

Storage granules (sometimes called inclusion granules) may occur within the cytoplasm of a cell. The main types of granules are shown in Table 2.1. Their number and size will vary according to the cultural conditions but in presence of an excess of an external energy source they can make up as much as 50%

**Table 2.1.** Storage granules in prokaryotes

| Granule | Main Component | Electron density | Suitable stain and reaction | Possible storage capacity |
|---|---|---|---|---|
| Polysaccharide | Glycogen | Transparent | Iodine-brown | C and energy |
| | Starch | Transparent | Iodine-dark blue | C and energy |
| Lipid | Poly-$\beta$-hydroxybutyrate | Transparent | Sudan black—black | C and energy |
| | Neutral lipid | Transparent | Sudan black—black | C and energy |
| Volutin | Polyphosphate | Opaque | Albert—purple | P and energy |
| Sulphur | Sulphur | Transparent | — | S and energy |

of the dry weight. Under deficient conditions they are broken down to provide useful cell building blocks, energy or both.

With the exception of poly-$\beta$-hydroxybutyrate and sulphur, these reserve polymers can also occur in eukaryotic cells.

## The cell wall

The cell wall is the dense layer surrounding the cytoplasmic membrane. Before considering its structure and function, it may be useful to digress and outline the most important differential staining method in microbiology used to separate bacteria into two fundamental groups—the Gram stain. There has been

17

much discussion concerning the biochemical basis of this staining method but it is probable that it is due to a difference in the porosity of the cell wall to the crystal-violet-iodine complex formed within it (Fig. 2.4), a difference that can be related to wall structure. Viewed in thin sections, Gram-positive bacteria have a thick amorphous single-layered structure (Plate 2.1, facing p. 16), while Gram-negatives normally show a much more complex multi-layered wall. In Gram-positives the main chemical component is the mucopeptide (see below) and this thick layer prevents removal of the crystal-violet-iodine complex by alcohol or acetone. In the Gram-negative cell wall the mucopeptide may only

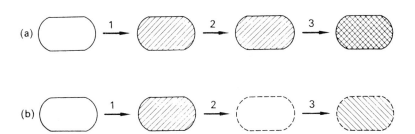

**Figure 2.4**  The probable mechanism of the Gram stain. (1) Treat with crystal violet and iodine. A crystal-violet-iodine complex is deposited within the cells. (2) Treat with alcohol or acetone. In Gram-negative cells, the crystal-violet-iodine complex is leached from the cells because of the greater porosity of the cell wall. (3) Counterstain with basic fuchsin. Gram-positive cells (a) are doubly stained to give a purple colour while Gram-negative cells (b) stain with basic fuchsin only

make up about 10% of the structure, the remainder being protein, polysaccharide and, in particular, lipid: alcohol treatment is likely to increase porosity by removing lipid and this together with the thin layer of mucopeptide gives rise to the differential staining.

Let us consider two particular wall components:

(1)  *The peptidoglycan* (mucopeptide, murein etc.). This is the most characteristic polymer in prokaryotes and is built up in a unique way by cross-linking polysaccharide chains by short polypeptides to give a vast macromolecule of the shape and size of the cell and of considerable mechanical strength. One of the most important aspects of the chemical structure is the presence of unique monomers in both the polysaccharide component (*N*-acetyl muramic acid) and the polypeptide component (D-amino acids and sometimes diaminopimelic acid). Apart from providing resistance to most degradative enzymes, this unique chemical structure is happily responsible for providing the basis for the action of many specific antibacterial agents of great value in medicine (see p. 103).

(2)  *The polysaccharides.* A very wide variety of polysaccharides occur in prokaryotes differing both in terms of monosaccharide components, some of which are peculiar to only a small group of bacteria, and in the way these mono-

18

saccharides are joined together. Such polysaccharides often occur on the outside of the wall and are therefore responsible for the surface properties of the cell.

*The function of the cell wall.* The main function of the wall is that of providing a mechanically strong bounding layer. Although a few prokaryotes do not have a cell wall, they can exist only in a very restricted range of protected habitats. The cell wall is not a semi-permeable membrane but it can act as a molecular sieve preventing large molecules passing through; in fact some enzymes may be trapped between the cytoplasmic membrane and the cell wall to form the *periplasm*.

## The capsule

Some prokaryotes have a gel layer called the capsule surrounding the cell wall. It can be seen in the light microscope by negative staining with a particulate dye incapable of penetrating it such as Indian ink, but is normally only visible as an amorphous shrunken layer in the electron microscope. The capsular gel is usually formed of a polysaccharide (1–2%) in water and as in cell-wall polysaccharides, there is a wide variety of different monosaccharide components joined in very many different ways. Occasionally capsules are made of polypeptide gels such as the peculiar polymer of the unusual D-glutamic acid found in the bacteria which cause the disease of anthrax.

The function of the capsule seems to be mainly as a protective layer against attack by phagocytes (see p. 98) and by viruses (see p. 75); it may also help to prevent too rapid and lethal a loss or gain of water in the recurrent dehydration and hydration that occurs in many habitats such as soil. Finally the capsule usually has an ion-exchange capacity which may aid in the concentration and uptake of essential cations.

## Flagella and locomotion

Most motile bacteria possess long thin (c. 20 nm diameter) extracellular appendages called flagella which are attached at one end through the cell wall to the cytoplasmic membrane by a special terminal hook and basal body. The individual flagellum is not visible using the light microscope without increasing its effective diameter by coating it with a suitable precipitate. In the electron microscope, negative-staining with phosphotungstic acid shows the flagellum to be made up of identical sub-units arranged helically along the axis of the flagellum to give a hollow tube. These sub-units can be separated from each other by acidification and consist of protein molecules called flagellin; neutralisation can cause automatic reaggregation to give a flagellum-like structure, a process presumably analogous to that occurring normally during flagellar growth. The arrangement and number of flagella on a cell can be a useful criterion for identification and classification (p. 35).

The function of flagella is in locomotion and all naturally occurring flagellate bacteria are motile. However, there are other less common types of motility in prokaryotes.

(a) *Gliding movement* which requires contact of the cell with a surface and probably involves some sort of contractile element built into the outer layers of the cell.

(b) *Spirochaetal movement.* The spirochaetes, a special group of bacteria have helically shaped cells with an axial filament or filament composed of flagellin-like elements built into the cell wall. Movement may occur through alternate expansion and contraction of this filament.

These two types of movement may represent more primitive forms of locomotion. Evolutionary separation of the contractile element from the wall except for an attachment at one end would produce a flagellum.

## Pili (fimbriae)

Prokaryotic cells may have appendages called pili or fimbriae and looking superficially similar to flagella. They too are built up of individual protein sub-units arranged helically to form a filament but they differ from flagella in numerous respects.

(a) The filament does not have the characteristic wavy form of flagella and is shorter.

(b) The diameter is smaller (about 10 nm).

(c) The function is not in motility. Some, the f-pili, occur only on male cells and act as a bridge through which DNA may pass in conjugation (p. 86). The function of others is more obscure but it is probable that they are mainly concerned as organs of attachment.

## Spores

As mentioned previously, some prokaryotes and especially those inhabiting soil, produce heat-resistant structures called spores. Characteristically a single endospore is formed within a vegetative cell and on germination a single vegetative cell is again produced.

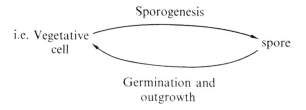

There has been much interest recently in this process since it provides a very simple model for the differentiation of one type of cell into another and could provide clues to the more complex processes occurring in animals and plants.

In the phase-contrast microscope, spores appear as highly refractile bodies sometimes greater in diameter than the cell from which they were formed while thin sections in the electron microscope show a complex multilayered wall (Fig. 2.5). Inside an exosporium of variable structure, there is a spore coat

20

composed of several laminated layers of protein. Below this is the thick cortex containing peplidoglycan, and, below it, the protoplast containing the most characteristic chemical component of the spore—a complex of calcium and dipicolinic acid which is thought to contribute to heat resistance.

Although the endospore is the typical resting stage in prokaryotes, two other forms can occur:

(1) *Cysts*. These are intermediate in structure and resistant properties between an endospore and a vegetative cell. An example of a cyst in a blue-green alga is seen in Plate 9.1, facing p. 110.

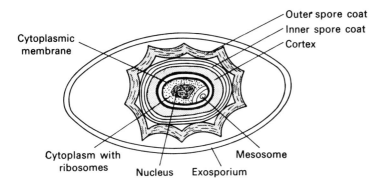

**Figure 2.5**  The structure of a typical bacterial endospore

(2) *Conidia (exospores)*. These are produced by fragmentation of the aerial ends of the multinucleate hyphae of the actinomycetes (p. 35). Because of the similarity to the mycelial structure and conidia formation in fungi, the actinomycetes used to be classed as fungi although it is now clear that they are made up of prokaryotic cells, albeit in a multinucleate and branched hyphal form.

## THE EUKARYOTIC CELL

Eukaryotic cells are generally much more complex in structure than prokaryotic cells. They are normally much larger with a typical diameter ten times greater (i.e. 10 $\mu$m), and they show a very great diversity in size and shape. However, we have a less complete knowledge of the various cell components compared with that of prokaryotic cells. It is very difficult to define a typical eukaryotic cell structure and it would probably be misleading to do so; the yeast presented in Fig. 2.6 and Plate 2.2, facing p. 16, should only be taken as an example of one type. Since most students will have an idea of the structure of some eukaryotic cells from their studies of Botany and Zoology, only some of the components will be mentioned in any detail and an emphasis will be placed on those structures that serve to distinguish the cells fundamentally from that of prokaryotes.

21

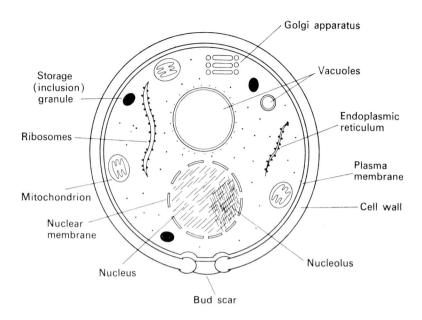

**Figure 2.6** A representation of a yeast cell

### Membranous structures

A variety of membranous semi-permeable structures occur within a eukaryotic cell giving a complex multi-compartmented whole.

(1) *The plasma membrane.* In both physical and chemical structure, the plasma membrane is very similar to the cytoplasmic membrane of prokaryotes. However, a striking difference is the presence of sterols in eukaryotic membranes. Further, the eukaryotic plasma membrane has only some of the functions of the prokaryotic cytoplasmic membrane—in particular that of a semi-permeable membrane. An additional function not possessed by prokaryotes can be the ability to ingest food in particulate form by *phagocytosis* or in liquid form by *pinocytosis;* in either case, a membrane-enclosed vacuole is formed within the cytoplasm (Fig. 2.7). Similar membranous vacuoles are the *lysozomes* in which are localised a variety of digestive enzymes.

(2) *Vacuoles.* The vacuoles concerned in food digestion have been mentioned in the previous section. They may also be involved in the accumulation and storage of metabolic intermediates whilst the contractile vacuoles occurring in some eukaryotes function in osmotic regulation and in the excretion of waste products. In contrast, the only vacuoles known to occur in prokaryotes are the rare gas vacuoles concerned as flotation devices, for example in blue-green algae (see Plate 9.1, facing p. 110).

(3) *Mitochondria and chloroplasts.* Instead of the energy-producing reactions

22

being localised in the external membrane of the cell, eukaryotes have specialised intracellular bodies surrounded by their own membranes to carry out phosphorylation.

Mitochondria are responsible for oxidative phosphorylation and have a size and structure reminiscent of a prokaryotic cell with an infolded cytoplasmic membrane. Indeed, some biologists believe that in the course of evolution

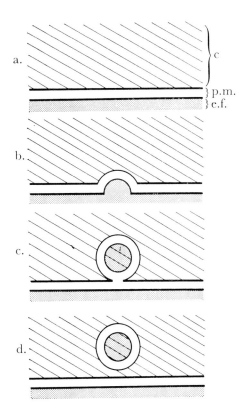

**Figure 2.7** A diagram of the processes of phagocytosis or pinocytosis in a eukaryotic cell. A portion of the fluid external to the cell (e.f.) and which may or may not contain particulate matter, is engulfed by the plasma membrane (p.m.) to form a vacuole in the cytoplasm (c.).

mitochondria have been derived by specialisation from an intracellular prokaryote which was parasitic (or symbiotic) in a primitive eukaryote. This intriguing idea has found support in the fact that mitochondria are capable of self-reproduction in the cell and contain within them a certain amount of DNA and ribosomes which are similar to those of prokaryotes rather than eukaryotes. Further, many present-day eukaryotes contain prokaryotes within them, some of which have undergone some degree of specialisation so that they can no longer exist outside the host cell. For example, paramecia contain bacteria-like particles which cannot be cultured outside the host eukaryote and can only be passed from one *Paramecium* to another by conjugation. The implications of this idea concerning mitochondrial evolution to more general schemes for the origin of microbial groups are discussed in Chapter 7.

Chloroplasts are membranous structures specialised for photosynthesis

23

which, like mitochondria, have their own DNA and ribosomes. Their size and shape varies widely amongst the different groups of algae and they, too, are thought to have arisen from primitive prokaryote symbionts or parasites which were also photosynthetic.

(4) *Nuclear membrane.* The eukaryotic nucleus is surrounded by a membrane containing pores to allow the passage of large molecules such as m-RNA.

(5) *Endoplasmic reticulum and Golgi bodies.* These membranes, although often fairly extensive within the cytoplasm, have been little studied. The endoplasmic reticulum is the site for ribosome attachment and it may also act as a communication or channelling system. The function of the Golgi bodies is less well understood but in some algae they may be involved in cell wall biosynthesis.

### The cytoplasm

Cytoplasmic streaming is common in eukaryotes but is said to be rare or absent in prokaryotes although their small size makes it very difficult to observe.

Eukaryotic ribosomes, although having an identical function to those of prokaryotes, have a somewhat larger sedimentation constant (80S) made up of sub-units of 60S and 40S. However, as has already been mentioned, the ribosomes occurring in mitochondria and chloroplasts have the same size as those of prokaryotes.

### The nucleus

In eukaryotic cells, the nucleus is a more definite structural entity surrounded by a membrane and containing many chromosomes. It is larger and contains a correspondingly large amount of DNA although the reason why all this extra DNA is required is unclear. The individual chromosomes appear to be made up of linear molecules of DNA compared with the circular DNA found in many prokaryotes. Associated with the nucleus there is normally an RNA-containing body called the nucleolus which seems to be a specialised structure responsible for ribosomal-RNA synthesis, a function carried out by the single chromosome of the prokaryotic nucleus. The eukaryotic chromosomes also differ in existing in alternative extended and contracted forms and in containing basic proteins called histones. Whereas prokaryotic DNA is normally synthesised during the whole division cycle, in eukaryotes production is limited to an average of about one-third of the cycle. This DNA doubling is followed in eukaryotes by the complicated process of mitosis designed to ensure an orderly partition of a complete set of chromosomes to each daughter cell.

### Storage granules

These have been described already (see p. 17).

24

## The cell wall

The cell walls of eukaryotic microorganisms vary widely in shape, in thickness and in chemical composition. Indeed most Protozoa apparently do not have walls at all although it is probable that they must have some additional strengthening of the plasma membrane to maintain cell shape and rigidity. When walls do occur, they can be isolated by a similar procedure to that mentioned previously (p. 12) and usually prove to have a simpler structure than those of prokaryotes.

(1) *Algae.* The basic structure is maintained by microfibrils formed by the intertwining of long cellulose molecules. Other homopolysaccharides may also occur such as polymannoses (mannans), polyxyloses (xylans) and polyuronic acids (pectins), while there are other algae with silica or calcium carbonate walls often sculptured into fascinating and beautiful shapes.

(2) *Fungi.* The common structural wall polymer is also a polyglucose but this time built of $1.\beta.3$ linkages compared with $1.\beta.4$ linkages of cellulose. The mechanical strength of the wall is probably maintained by $1.\beta.6$ cross linkages to give a thick and tough structure similar to the prokaryotic mucopeptide wall. Polymannoses are also common in fungal walls as are poly-$N$-acetylglucosamines similar to the chitin of invertebrates.

(3) *Protozoa.* Usually protozoa have no definite wall although some have structures built from cellulose, calcium carbonate, silica or strontium sulphate.

## Flagella, cilia and locomotion

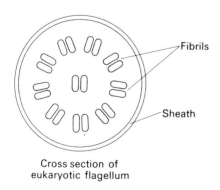

Cross section of
eukaryotic flagellum

The movement of eukaryotic microorganisms is usually by the action of flagella or cilia which have a structure quite different from that of the prokaryote flagellum. They are much wider, are surrounded by a sheath and have many fibrils each of which is similar in structure to the prokaryotic flagellum. Another method of locomotion in eukaryotic microorganisms is by amoeboid movement, a result of cytoplasmic streaming in cells not having a cell wall. Motile eukaryotes often show movement towards or away from heat, light or certain chemical substances; these phenomena are less common in prokaryotes.

25

# COMPARISON OF PROKARYOTIC AND EUKARYOTIC CELLS

The result of the structural studies outlined in this chapter has been to show that prokaryotic and eukaryotic cells differ in many different aspects and these are summarised in Table 2.2.

**Table 2.2.** A comparison of the main distinguishing features between prokaryotic and eukaryotic cells.

| | Prokaryotic cell | Eukaryotic cell |
|---|---|---|
| Typical diameter | 1 μm | 10 μm |
| Number of chromosomes | 1 | Greater than 1 |
| Nuclear membrane | — | + |
| Mitosis | — | + |
| No. of compartments | Usually 1 | Greater than 1 |
| Oxidative phosphorylation site | Cytoplasmic membrane | Mitochondria |
| Photosynthetic phosphorylation site | Cytoplasmic membrane | Chloroplasts |
| Vacuoles | Rare | Common |
| Cytoplasmic Ribosome size | 70S | 80S |
| Peptidoglycan | Usually present | Absent |
| Flagella | 1 Fibril | Many fibrils + membrane |
| Sexual reproduction | Rare and incomplete | Common and complete |

# THE STRUCTURE OF VIRUSES

We have left to the last discussion of a group of organisms which have a simpler structure to both eukaryotic and prokaryotic cells and are generally considered as non-cellular or *akaryotic*.

Viruses are smaller than the limit of resolution of the light microscope and before the development of the electron microscope their existence could only be inferred by the ability of preparations to cause disease after they had been passed through a filter with a porosity low enough to remove cellular organisms (c. 0·2 μm pores). In other words, the term virus was synonymous with a filter-passing infective agent. It was shown that viruses attacked a wide range of living organisms in the microbial, animal and plant kingdoms. Growth could be measured in terms of an increase in infectivity and it was soon found that it only occurred within a host. Methods were developed to purify the virus particles and in 1935 Stanley obtained the tobacco mosaic virus in a crystalline state. This was a revolutionary step since it showed that many of the properties of viruses were those of the high molecular weight polymers studied by biochemists; similar methods could therefore be used in their study and purification. With the advent of the electron microscope it became possible to study the morphology of viruses and to correlate the results with chemical analyses of purified preparations.

26

The usual method of naming viruses is to describe the host and usually the symptoms of the disease caused. A virus attacking tobacco plants and causing bleaching of chlorophyll in spots on the leaves is thus called tobacco mosaic virus; one isolated from the adenoids of a man is called a human adenovirus; one attacking *Escherichia coli* is called an *Escherichia coli* bacteriophage or a coliphage for short. Different strains may be given letters and numbers such as the series of T coliphages (p. 73) associated with many basic experiments in molecular biology. The reason for this classification is that one based on morphology would be almost valueless. Indeed, viruses attacking quite different hosts may appear morphologically indistinguishable, as are the human poliomyelitis and the turnip yellow mosaic viruses. Recently attempts have been made to introduce a binominal system of nomenclature but fortunately this has not yet been generally accepted.

## The size and shape of viruses

As soon as it became possible to view viruses in the electron microscope, three generalisations emerged.

(1) A wide variety of different shapes and sizes occurred ranging from the f2 coliphage with a roughly spherical shape and a diameter of 20 nm, through the complex tailed phages to the vaccinia virus with a brick shape of 250 × 300 nm.

(2) The individual particles of a particular virus were identical in size and shape. The revolutionary implications of this fact were only slowly realised by most virologists for the startling conclusion must be that viruses do not grow and multiply but must somehow be formed *de novo*.

(3) The use of negative-staining methods led to an over-all picture of virus structure consisting of a central nucleic acid core surrounded by a protein coat called a *capsid*, which is itself made up of individual units called *capsomeres*. This invariable structure (sometimes called a nucleo-capsid) can be further surrounded by an envelope. On the basis of the way in which capsomeres are assembled to make up a capsid and of the presence or absence of an envelope, it is possible to distinguish four main types of virus organisation given in Fig. 2.8, as well as a few more complex designs.

*Naked icosahedrons.* Careful study of the so-called spherical viruses showed that they are all icosahedral in shape, that is they are made up of a structure with 20 triangular faces and 12 vertices. This shape is determined by the individual protein capsomeres which are arranged according to the laws of geometry and crystallography. The simplest theoretical design is one with 12 identical capsomeres to form the 12 vertices as in the coliphage of ΦX 174. The next permissible number is 32 capsomeres of which 12 are required for the vertices and 20 for the face units. The next number is 72 with 12 corner units and 3 for each face unit, i.e. 12 + (3 × 20), and so on, the largest known number being in the Tipula irridescent virus of insects with 812 capsomeres (i.e. 12 + (40 × 20)). It is fascinating to note that exactly similar principles are used

27

in the building of geodesic domes where a very strong design can be got from quite light and easily assembled units. The nucleic acid of these viruses is located in a very condensed form inside the capsid. An example of a naked icosahedral virus is shown in Plates 2.3a and b.

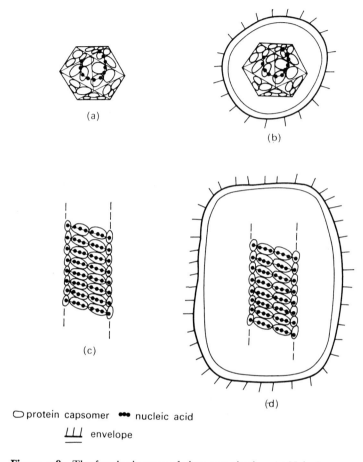

O protein capsomer ••• nucleic acid

⊔⊔⊔ envelope

**Figure 2.8** The four basic types of virus organisation. (a) Naked icosahedral (b) enveloped icosahedron, (c) naked helical, (d) enveloped helical

*Naked helices.* In the helical viruses, the individual capsomeres are arranged spirally so that the final capsid is a hollow tube. The individual capsomeres are identical and the nucleic acid is located in a helical groove on the inside of the cylindrical capsid. An example is shown in Plate 2.3c.

*Enveloped viruses.* Either the helical or the icosahedral type of virus is sometimes surrounded by a loose membranous envelope. Most enveloped viruses attack animals and the envelope seems to be partly derived from the host plasma membrane. An example is shown in Plate 2.3d.

28

*Complex viruses.* A few viruses have a more complex structure than those described above. The best analysed examples are the tailed bacteriophages and, in particular, the coliphages (p. 27 and Plate 2.4, facing p. 17). Whereas the head of the phage is an almost conventional icosahedron containing the viral nucleic acid there is a very complex tail structure attached to it containing at least five different protein types making up the sheath, core, collar, end plate and fibres. However, all these structures are formed by the condensation of sub-units by a process analagous to crystallisation. The importance of this will be realised when virus replication is discussed in Chapter 7.

## The chemical composition of viruses

There are two basic chemical components in viruses—protein and nucleic acid. In many viruses they are the sole components and as will be discussed in Chapter 7, it is only the nucleic acid which is necessary for viral reproduction, the protein being concerned in the transference of the nucleic acid from one cell to another.

(1) *Protein.* Viral proteins contain the same amino acids in similar proportions to those of cellular forms of life. Most, if not all, of the protein has a structural function and makes up the individual capsomeres which are themselves usually made up of identical or nearly identical sub-units. The capsid so produced acts as a protective sheath round the nucleic acid. Occasionally enzymes occur as a part of the viral structure but their function is solely in facilitating the entry of the viral nucleic acid into the host cell; an example of such an enzyme is the lysozyme-like enzyme of the bacteriophage tail (p. 75).

(2) *Nucleic acid.* Either RNA or DNA can occur but they are never present in the same organism, a characteristic immediately separating viruses from cellular forms of life which always have both RNA and DNA. Although viral DNA is usually double-stranded and viral RNA is usually single-stranded, a few viruses contain either single-stranded DNA or double-stranded RNA. In any case, the nucleic acid is usually present as a single thread (chromosome) which may be circular and contain anything from a few thousand to almost 250,000 nucleotide units. This gives a nucleic content varying from as little as 1% in the influenza virus to as much as 50% in certain bacteriophages.

(3) *Other viral constituents.* The main additional component is the lipid found in some enveloped animal viruses where it can vary considerably in amount between about 5% and 50%. Polysaccharides can also occur in enveloped viruses but both they and the lipid may represent host components incorporated into the virus in its passage out through the plasma membrane. It becomes even more difficult to determine whether some of the lower molecular weight components found in some virus preparations are 'true' structural elements or whether they are simply derived from the host cell. However, polyamines such as spermine or spermidine are often present in reproducible

29

amounts and probably serve to neutralise the acid groups of the nucleic acid and to facilitate as close packing as possible within the capsid. ATP and calcium ions are bound into the tail of the bacteriophage and are thought to aid in the contraction process involved in cell entry (see p. 75).

## The differentiation of viruses from prokaryotic and eukaryotic cells

It should be clear from what has been said that even in their structure and chemical composition viruses are quite different from the two types of cells. It is easier to consider all the differentiating characters when virus reproduction has been discussed in Chapter 7, but the very simple and uniform structure, the presence of only one form of nucleic acid and the absence of normal metabolic enzymes make it clear that they are a quite distinct group. Contrary to earlier belief, there appear to be no forms intermediate between viruses and cellular life, the implication being that viruses arose by the evolution of cell organelles rather than by the gradual simplification of a parasitic cell. This idea is discussed later.

# 3 A survey of microorganisms

Before considering the vast range of microorganisms occurring in nature, a general word must be said about the patterns of nomenclature, identification and classification. The object of nomenclature is simply to be able to give an organism a name while the object of classification or taxonomy is to arrange the named organisms into orderly groups that reflect the similarities within a group and the differences from other groups. If we are solely concerned with identification as for example in the diagnosis of a disease, then the characters employed in this identification should be easy to measure, should be reproducible in a variety of laboratories and should give a *useful* identification with as few characters as possible. In other words, we want to produce a key which is valuable with respect to the original purpose of a practical identification. Most microbial taxonomy is of this type and inevitably some characters are considered more important than others simply because they are more useful. A *phylogenetic taxonomy* based on the evolutionary relationships of microorganisms is unfortunately (or some might say fortunately) not possible due to lack of evidence. Microbial fossils can provide little detailed evidence and the more sophisticated molecular biological studies are only in their infancy. However, there have been recent attempts to create a classification based on more than mere convenience. *Numerical taxonomy* uses as many characters as possible, each of which is given an equal weight. The results are fed into a computer so as to define the similarities and differences between microorganisms and thus to define natural groupings.

Let us consider some of the characters that are used by the microbiologist.

(1) *Morphological characters.* These have been discussed in the previous chapter and concern cell shape and size, staining reactions, presence or absence of spores or reproductive forms, type of motility, etc.

(2) *Cultural characters.* These include the cultural requirements for multiplication (e.g. nutrients, oxygen, temperature, etc.) and the way growth occurs in liquid media and, particularly, on solid media (e.g. colony form).

(3) *Biochemical characters.* More specific biochemical properties such as the metabolic end-products and the presence or absence of a particular enzyme or pathway.

(4) *Serological characters.* The nature of the surface antigens as revealed by suitable specific antibodies (see p. 99).

(5) *Molecular characters.* New approaches to classification have become available with the development of molecular biology. For example, we can use factors relating to DNA composition; although the amount of adenine (A) equals that of thymine (T) and the amount of guanine (G) that of cytosine (C), there is a considerable amount of variation in the ratio of G + C to A + T.

Granted some sort of taxonomic system, how should a microorganism be named? It is usual to use a binominal system; each distinct species is given a name consisting of two words—the first is the genus and is written with a capital letter while the second is the specific epithet (the species) and is not capitalised. Sometimes species are further divided into varieties or strains, e.g. *Escherichia* (genus) *coli* (species) $K$ *12* (strain).

It is evident that once even a simple binominal nomenclature is used, an hierarchical sceme is implied and three questions must be asked.

(a) How is a species defined?

(b) How many species should be grouped into a single genus and what should be the criteria for this grouping?

(c) Should genera be similarly grouped to produce a multi-tiered hierarchical classification?

Let us consider these questions briefly with particular respect to bacteria.

(a) *The species*. Sexual reproduction rarely occurs and, if it does, it is often of such a primitive nature as to prevent any definition of species on the basis of an ability to conjugate. Further, microorganisms are commonly haploid and are often subject to high selective pressures; in other words the evolution of different forms can be very rapid in response to a change in environment (see p. 83). All we can do is to take a *useful* selection of common characters and use them to define a species.

(b) *The genus*. Likewise, a grouping of species into genera must be a practical one in the absence of phylogenetic information. Again a grouping of similar characters must be used, more restricted and possibly more fundamental than that for the species. It must be admitted that the very vagueness of the concept of genus has led to vast differences in the way it is used. Thus the genus *Bacillus* includes all aerobic, rod-shaped, endospore-forming, Gram-positive bacteria and a wide range of species occur; on the other hand the genus *Salmonella* is restricted to a group of bacteria pathogenic for man and other animals which, apart from the type of disease caused and the specific chemistry of surface antigens, differ very little.

Rather to the surprise of the more cynical microbiologist, the use of the computer in numerical taxonomy has given support to the concept of species and, to a lesser extent, of genus. In other words, bacteria do fall into natural groupings although the reason for this may well be that they inhabit similar environmental niches to which they have become adapted; this adaptation has in itself selected certain characteristics.

(c) *Families*, etc. It is common to group genera together and so on up through an hierarchical taxonomy with the following divisions: Species; Genera; (Tribes); Families; (Suborders); Orders; Classes. It is, of course, attractive to the tidy-minded to produce such a system but since it cannot aid the identification or nomenclature of an organism, the only real justification must be a phylogenetic one. Since we do not know enough about microbial evolution, it

32

is questionable how useful to the student it is to have any intermediate groupings in prokaryotic organisms between that of bacteria and blue-green algae at one end and the individual genera at the other end. The major sub-divisions of the chief groups of eukaryotic microorganisms (algae, fungi and protozoa) are sometimes more justifiable but again it can be argued that the phylogenetic evidence is lacking.

## PROKARYOTIC MICROORGANISMS

How can we sub-divide the prokaryotes? Although there might be some logic in considering prokaryotes and bacteria as being synonymous, the discovery that blue-green algae are also prokaryotes has confused the situation. For the purpose of this book, we will use the term blue-green algae as meaning prokaryotes carrying out an oxygen-evolving type of photosynthesis and call all other prokaryotes bacteria. It is true that there are greater differences between the bacteria than there are between some bacteria and blue-green algae, but it is difficult to make the latter name redundant for historical reasons. Can we subdivide bacteria into major groupings? Although this is often done, we have already pointed out the artificiality of formally doing so given our present knowledge. Some groupings will be mentioned (e.g. myxobacteria, nitrogen-fixing bacteria, spirochaetes) without any phylogenetic implications on the reality of such a grouping beyond the important one of convenience.

Let us consider the range of prokaryotic microorganisms in terms of their structure leaving the more biochemical and genetic aspects to the appropriate chapters.

### Cell shapes

There are three basic cell shapes

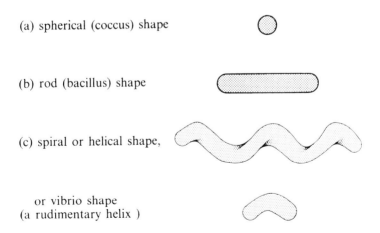

(a) spherical (coccus) shape

(b) rod (bacillus) shape

(c) spiral or helical shape,

or vibrio shape
(a rudimentary helix )

## Multicellular structures

Sometimes cell division and cross-wall formation are not followed by the separation of the daughter cells. In this way an undifferentiated multicellular structure is produced, the shape of which will depend upon the planes of cell division. Thus rods always divide in one plane and, if the cells remain attached, a multicellular filament is formed.

i.e.

An example is seen in the blue-green algae (Fig. 9.2, p. 111).
In spherical cells a variety of shapes can occur:
   (a) cells divide in one plane and remain predominantly attached in pairs

e.g. Diplococci

   (b) cells divide in one plane and remain attached to form chains

e.g. Streptococci

   (c) cells divide in two planes to give plates

e.g. Pediococci

   (d) cells divide in three planes regularly to produce a cube

e.g. Sarcina

(e) cells divide in three planes irregularly producing bunches of cocci

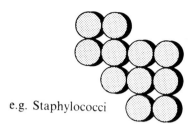

e.g. Staphylococci

Spiral bacteria are predominantly unattached but the individual cells of different species show striking differences in length and in tightness of spiral.

In all these instances, the multicellular form is made up of separate individual cells. However, in actinomycetes multinucleate cells without cross walls produce branched mycelia of indefinite length which appear superficially similar to those of filamentous fungi

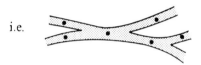

i.e.

## Spores and cysts

Spores and cysts have already been discussed in Chapter 2 (p. 20). Their occurrence and their position in the cell are often used as distinguishing characters.

## Motility

As discussed previously (p. 19), prokaryotic motility may be by flagella, by gliding or by an axial filament. If it is by flagella, the arrangement of the flagella may be a useful diagnostic feature

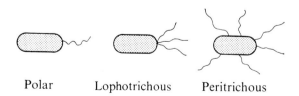

Polar          Lophotrichous       Peritrichous

## Stalks

A few bacteria have a stalk by which they attach to a solid substratum using a holdfast at the tip.

This attachment is usually a stable one and on cell division a flagellate cell is produced which swims around, eventually settling on a new surface where it forms a stalk in place of the flagellum. Thus it has a primitive life cycle ensuring an attached and a swarming phase.

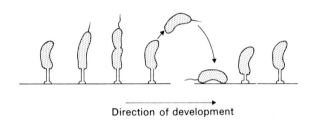

Direction of development

## Buds

The majority of bacteria divide by binary fission in which the cell gradually doubles in size, divides into two equal halves, each of which goes on to repeat the process. However, a few divide by budding, a process analagous to that characteristic of yeasts.

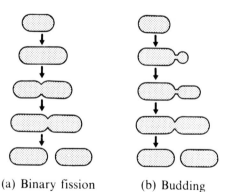

(a) Binary fission　　　(b) Budding

An interesting feature of binary fission as distinct from budding is that there is no parent and offspring in the normal sense and ageing apparently cannot occur.

## Absence of cell wall

Some bacteria usually called mycoplasmas are incapable of forming a peptidogly-can cell wall. They are consequently highly pleomorphic because of the lack of wall rigidity and are prone to lysis even though the cytoplasmic membrane may be partially strengthened by substances like sterols derived from the host. Prob-ably mycoplasmas are much more widespread in nature than was thought and they can commonly be isolated from warm-blooded animals including man and from plants. Since they have probably evolved by a loss in wall-forming ability in a variety of bacteria, they differ in many important characters and illustrate the danger of grouping organisms on the basis of a single character.

## Intracellular parasites of eukaryotes

A variety of bacteria can parasitise eukaryotes. The most interesting are those which have lost the capacity for growth outside the host cell. They show a very primitive biosynthetic machinery and it is assumed that their evolution into a strictly parasitic existence has allowed a considerable simplification in the enzymes and therefore genes required (p. 72). As a result of this simplification the cells are much smaller and may have a diameter of only about 0·3 $\mu$m. This may well be about as small as a cellular form of life can be since there is a limit on the degree of reliance that can be placed on the host cell without going to a viral organisation. Certainly organisms of the type considered here (rickettsias and chlamydia) contain both DNA and RNA and have most of the characteristics of prokaryotic cells.

## Intracellular parasites of prokaryotes

Recently a group of small highly motile bacteria have been found that are parasites of other prokaryotes. They adhere to the wall of the host, penetrate through to the cytoplasm where they replicate and eventually cause the lysis of the host cell. Organisms like this are called bdellovibrios and are probably common in environments like the soil.

## Fruiting bacteria

A few bacteria called myxobacteria have the property of forming fruiting bodies, specialised multicellular structures reminiscent of some of those pro-duced by fungi. Under appropriate conditions such as nutrient deficiencies, a swarm of vegetative cells aggregate and form a fruiting body with a shape characteristic of the species. Some of the cells at the tips of the fruiting body then undergo differentiation to produce cysts.

These fruiting myxobacteria present the most complex behavioural patterns and life cycles found in prokaryotes. Much interest has been shown in them since the process of fruiting body formation could provide a primitive and simple system to answer the following questions of key importance to an understanding of higher form of life.

(a) What causes cell differentiation? We have already mentioned that the process of sporulation in prokaryotes represents an even simpler system.

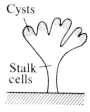

Cysts

Stalk cells

(b) What causes cells to aggregate to produce a multicellular structure?

(c) What determines the shape of such a multicellular structure?

## EUKARYOTIC MICROORGANISMS

The three groups of eukaryotic microorganisms are the fungi, the algae and the protozoa (a fourth group—the myxomycetes—are sometimes separated). Although it is possible to distinguish clearly the characteristics of the typical members of these groups, there are intermediate forms. Indeed it is exceedingly difficult to lay down a clear set of distinguishing characteristics. Eukaryotic microorganisms have tended to lie in a no-man's land between the more characteristic organisms studied by the microbiologist (bacteria and viruses) and by the botanist and zoologist (higher plants and animals). Yeasts are the only organisms that have to some extent escaped this fate because of their economic importance and their relative simplicity. This lack of knowledge is unfortunate as many eukaryotic microorganisms provide a fascinating and vast range of different organisms which will undoubtedly become better known in the future. Possibly such developments will result in a realisation that too many disparate groups have been lumped together into the present three major groups.

### The fungi

Let us consider some of the typical characteristics of filamentous fungi.

(1) They are heterotrophic eukaryotic microorganisms obtaining their food in a soluble form by uptake through the plasma membrane in a manner similar to that of prokaryotes.

(2) They have a thick cell wall usually made of simple polysaccharides (see p. 25).

(3) They have a typically branched growth or *mycelium* made up of individual filaments called *hyphae*. The intertwined mycelia are produced by branching behind the hyphal tips during growth or by hyphal fusion; in some cases the aggregated hyphae may form large structures which bear a superficial resemblance to the tissues of higher plants (e.g. in mushrooms and toadstools).

38

(4) Mycelia are *coenocytic*—that is they are composed of multinucleate tubes with the cytoplasm in continuous connection throughout. Some mycelia have no cross walls while others have septa with pores to allow cytoplasmic connection.

(5) The majority are adapted to life in the soil where they are important in converting organic carbon to $CO_2$. The major part of the organism (the

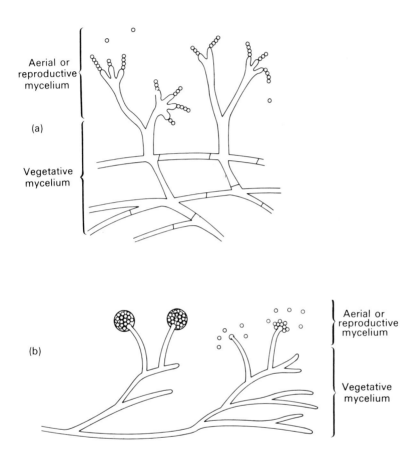

**Figure 3.1** Two types of asexual spore production and two types of vegetative mycelia. (a) *Penicillium* with asexual spores as conidia. (b) *Mucor* with asexual spores in a sporangium and the vegetative mycelium.

*vegetative mycelium*) is concerned with the uptake of nutrients and attachment to a solid surface (Fig. 3.1).

(6) From the vegetative mycelium specialised aerial hyphae are produced and from these *asexual spores* are differentiated. The spores may arise as single cells at hyphal tips (*conidiospores* or *conidia*) or inside a structure called a *sporangium* (Fig. 3.1). Sometimes spores are produced within a hypha by a

39

process analagous to endospore production in bacteria to produce resting spores (*chlamydospores*). While the vegetative mycelium is normally colourless, the aerial or reproductive mycelia are often brightly coloured. The whole process has a function of dispersal since each fungus produces enormous numbers of these light spores which are easily carried from one place to another by air currents.

(7) *Sexual spores* (Fig. 3.2) can also be produced, as the result of sexual reproduction. A large variety of structures may be found to hold these sexual spores and the 'fruiting bodies' may be of considerable complexity. As a result of sexual reproduction, there is an alternation of haploid and diploid cells and this alternation may give rise to a complex life cycle (see p. 88). It is obvious that many types of spore-bearing structures can occur in fungi and great use is made of them in classification.

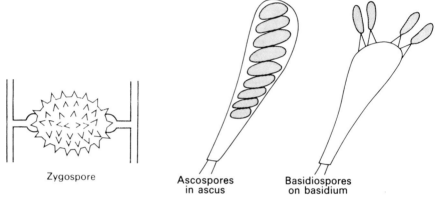

Zygospore

Ascospores
in ascus

Basidiospores
on basidium

**Figure 3.2** Different types of sexual spores in fungi

Although the majority of fungi produce multicellular hyphae as indicated above, a few are characteristically unicellular. These are the *yeasts* which show signs of their evolutionary origin by their ability under certain cultural conditions to produce chains of cells resembling hyphae and called *pseudomycelia;* many can also produce asexual and sexual spores. Their normal mode of multiplication is by budding although there are a few which divide by binary fission. Yeasts are most commonly found in sugary environments where they carry out their famed alcoholic fermentation (see p. 114).

### The algae

It would be difficult to underestimate the importance of algae to fresh-water or marine environments. They can occur in such large amounts in the surface layers that the water appears coloured. In the oceans where they form a major part of the plankton, the total mass of algae is probably greater than that of all our landplants, and they are responsible for over half of the over-all rate of the biosynthesis of organic compounds from $CO_2$. Although algae mainly occur in waters, some grow in soil or on the surface of vegetation provided that the environment remains reasonably moist. In drier situations, algae have to be

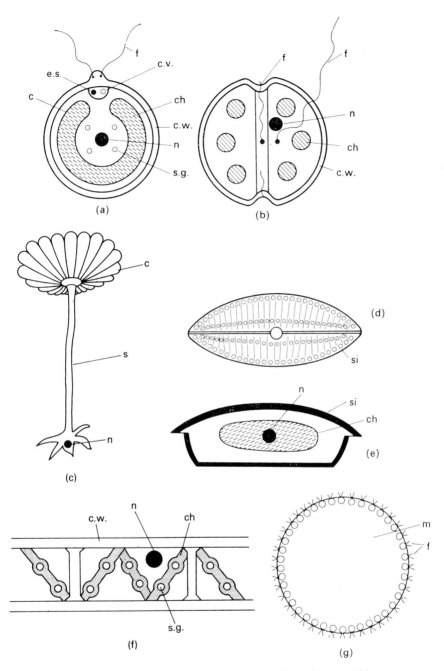

**Figure 3.3** Some algae. a–e Unicellular algae. (a) *Chlamydomonas*, (b) *Gymnodinium*, (c) Acetabularia, (d) a diatom—top view of silica shell, (e) cross section of diatom, (f) a filamentous alga—*Spirogyra*, (g) cross section of a colonial algae—*Volvox*. c, cap; c.v., contractile vacuole; c.w., cell wall; ch, chloroplast; e.s., eye spot; f. flagella; m, gelatinous matrix; n, nucleus; s.g., storage granule; s, stalk; si, silica shell

protected from desiccation by association with fungus hyphae to form lichens (p. 95).

What are the characteristic properties of algae?

(1) They obtain their energy by an oxygen-producing photosynthesis occurring in chloroplasts. Within the chloroplasts, which show a great diversity in shape and number per cell, are found a variety of chlorophylls which are often characteristic of the algal group.

(2) They exhibit a wide range of morphological types. Although some are unicellular, others produce cell aggregates embedded in mucilage; still others produce filaments which may be multicellular or coenocytic. Some algae such as the seaweeds have a very complex, almost plant-like, colonial structure, although there is no cellular differentiation in the sense of its occurrence in higher animals and plants. It should be noted that some brown algae like the oceanic kelps are far from being microscopic and may reach a length of 50 m.

Some of the single-celled algae are fascinating in the size and complexity of a single cell. Thus an *Acetabularia* cell has a root-like base, a stalk several centimetres long and an umbrella-shaped cap (Fig. 3.3c). It has been used as a test organism in studying nuclear-cytoplasmic relationships as the very large nucleus is located in the base and can be easily removed. Nucleolated portions can regenerate a complete structure, but even a non-nucleolated region can regenerate a stalk and cap provided a reasonable amount of cytoplasm remains; this shows that stable cytoplasmic components (presumably long-lived m-RNA) can control regeneration.

(3) Many algae are motile usually by flagella. In a colonial alga such as *Volvox* (Fig. 3.3f), as many as 50,000 individual flagellated cells may make up a complex structure in which the action of the flagella is highly coordinated throughout the colony. On the other hand, diatoms are said to carry out some form of jet propulsion.

(4) Algae characteristically have a thick cell wall of cellulose, although there are commonly additional components such as pectin, xylan and calcium carbonate. Some of the most fascinating walls are the silica shells of diatoms which exhibit a wide variety of beautiful shapes. These silica shells remain after the death of the organisms and they can accumulate as vast fossil deposits of so-called diatomaceous earth which may be as much as 1,000 m thick.

(5) Algae can reproduce either sexually or asexually and can show very complicated life cycles.

Over 17,000 different kinds of algae have been described and a few of these are illustrated in Fig. 3.3.

## The protozoa

The protozoa are commonly defined simply as unicellular animals. This is not a very helpful definition for the microbiologist and perhaps it would be better to say that they are a group of unicellular, non-photosynthetic eukaryotic microorganisms which normally obtain their food by phagocytosis and which

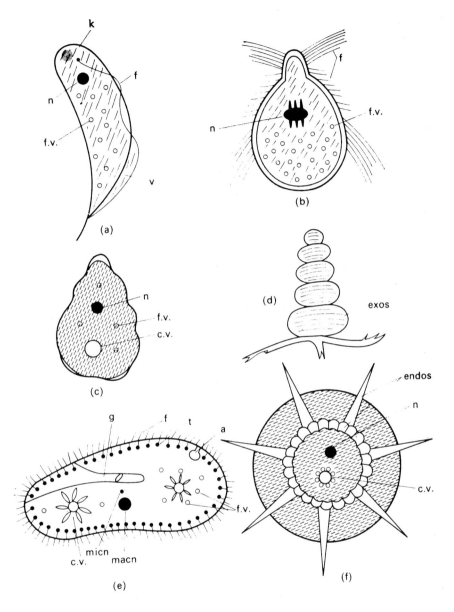

**Figure 3.4** Some protozoa (a) trypanosome, (b) *Trichonympha*. Amoecoid forms, (c) *Amoeba*, (d) a foraminiferan, (e) *Paramecium*. a, anal pore; c, cilia; c.v., contractile vacuole; exos, exoskeleton; endos, endoskeleton; f.v., food vacuole; f, flagellum; g, gullet; k, kinetosome; m, mouth; n, nucleus; macn, macronucleus; micn, micronucleus; ps, pseudopodiuu; t, trichocyst; u, undulating membrane. (f) a radiolarian.

possess no true cell wall. Some examples of protozoa are shown in Fig. 3.4 and a few of their characteristics will now be considered.

(1) The type of *movement* can be used to divide the protozoa into major groupings.

(a) Amoeboid motion is characteristic of organisms similar to *Amoeba* (Fig. 3.4c). Cytoplasm flows forward into a pseudopodium which is produced in the direction of movement on a solid surface; the opposite end of the cell is correspondingly retracted.

(b) Flagellar movement occurs in the flagellate protozoa, some of which are the colourless counterparts of particular algae. Since chloroplasts have their own DNA, their loss by a cell will be irreversible and a non-photosynthetic form which would be normally classed as a flagellate protozoan will result. This process illustrates the hazy borderlines between the major groups of eukaryotic microorganisms. Some protozoa have a simple flagellum while others have a very complex flagellar arrangement as in *Trichonympha* (Fig. 3.4b), an organism inhabiting the guts of termites where it is responsible for the digestion of the cellulose in the wood eaten by the insects.

(c) Ciliary movement in ciliates which are usually covered over much of the cell surface with cilia which, although similar in structure to flagella, are shorter and have a coordinated motion so that waves of contraction pass over them.

(2) *Food* is characteristically taken up by the *phagocytosis* of solid particles such as bacteria. This digestion leads to the formation of a food vacuole in which digestion occurs, the indigestible material being liberated on the surface by evagination.

In some protozoa such as amoebae there are no specialised areas on the surface, whereas ciliates usually have a 'mouth' for food uptake and an 'anus' for exit (Fig. 3.4f).

(3) Protozoa generally have no cell wall. However, some amoeboid forms have a solid structure which can best be described as a skeleton since it may be internal or external and has pores to allow for food uptake by phagocytosis. The marine Foraminifera have complicated and multichambered calcium carbonate exoskeletons (Fig. 3.4d), which, like those of diatoms, can form geological deposits of chalk. Others (the radiolaria) have an endoskeleton of silica or strontium sulphate (Fig. 3.4e).

(4) The protozoa usually have a less complicated life cycle than other algae or fungi, but there are some exceptions such as the parasitic protozoa (e.g. the organism causing malaria).

(5) One of the most interesting aspects is the degree of specialisation that can occur in a single cell. To take the well-known example of the unicellular *Paramecium* (Fig. 3.4f), there is a specialised food uptake system with gullet and mouth, an anus, contractile vacuoles, cilia and trichocysts on the surface attached to kinetosomes which are self-replicating DNA bodies, and a complicated nuclear system containing both a micronucleus and a macronucleus. Organisms like *Paramecium* seem to represent the end-limit to which specialisation of a single cell can go, the more fruitful evolutionary development being

44

in the differentiation between the cells of multi-cellular organisms to form tissues.

### The slime moulds (myxomycetes)

The slime moulds are a group that have been claimed as fungi and as protozoa although it is probably better to consider them separately. They are non-photosynthetic eukaryotic microorganisms resembling protozoa in having an amoeboid vegetative form and resembling fungi in their sporing stages. They live on the surface of decaying vegetation and often produce brightly coloured and ornate fruiting bodies. There are two groups, the cellular slime moulds

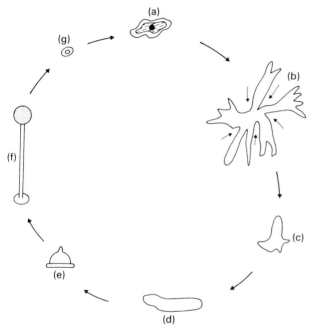

**Figure 3.5** The life cycle of a cellular slime mould. Vegetative amoeboid cells (a) aggregate together, (b) to form a pseudoplasmodium (c) which migrates (d) to form a fruiting body (e-f) which produces asexual spores (g).

whose vegetative stage consists of single amoeboid cells which can aggregate to form a *pseudoplasmodium* and the acellular slime moulds where a single amoeba produces a multinucleate plasmodium of indefinite size and shape which moves over the surface of a substratum engulfing food particles as it goes. The latter group represents the type of microorganisms most beloved of the science fiction writer.

Let us consider the life history of a cellular slime mould (Fig. 3.5). The vegetative amoebae feed on particulate matter; when the supply of food is exhausted, they aggregate into pseudoplasmodial groups, a process triggered by the secretion of a hormone-like substance called *acrasin* which attracts cells together by a chemotactic response. The pseudoplasmodium moves towards the light as a single unit surrounded by a mucoid sheet secreted by the individual cells until eventually movement ceases. The multicellular structure then differentiates to produce a fruiting body involving the formation of a sheath by the external cells forming cellulose while other cells pass up through the sheath and, on reaching the top of the body, are converted to spores which are dispersed into the environment where they eventually germinate to start the process again. The similarity between these organisms and the myxobacteria should be noted, the result of a presumed convergent evolution. They, too, have been used as model systems for answering the questions outlined for the myxobacteria on p. 37.

# 4 The growth of cellular microorganisms

In a unicellular microorganism multiplying by binary fission, a new cell grows to double its size and then divides into two equal parts that repeat the process. Growth, which can be defined as the orderly increase in all the constituents of a cell, is going on all the time, whereas multiplication is only occurring at the instant of cell division. This can be seen in the growth and multiplication of a single cell (Fig. 4.1) and the same result occurs in a synchronously dividing population of cells (see p. 52). However, the microbiologist is normally dealing with a very large number of cells. For example,

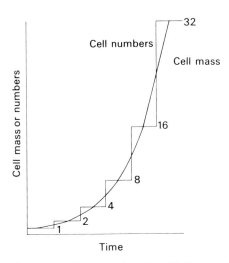

**Figure 4.1**  The growth and multiplication of a single cell

a bacterial colony on an agar plate contains about $10^8$ cells, a suspension of $10^8$ cells per ml will be only just visibly turbid whilst 1 mg dried bacteria contains about $3 \times 10^9$ cells. With such large populations, the chances are that the percentage of cells dividing in any one small period of time will be the same as that in any other period and if we plot growth or multiplication against time, we will get the same curve. In other words, the cells in the culture are dividing asynchronously. Consequently we can normally consider growth and multiplication as being synonymous and we can measure whichever is most practicable.

In order to study multiplication, the actual number of organisms must be measured. The straightforward way to do this is to use a counting chamber under the microscope but this simple process immediately brings up a problem. How do we tell whether the organisms we see under the microscope are dead or alive? This leads to another problem. When does a 'live' microorganism become 'dead'? Fortunately the question as applied to microbial life has no overriding philosophic or religious overtones and we can seek a useful answer. In fact the only practical one is that we call an organism living (or *viable*) if it is capable of a continuing division. It is dead (or *non-viable*) if it cannot multiply. This brings us back to the original question—how can we tell under a microscope if a cell is viable? Although staining methods have been developed that show some correlation with viability, the fair answer is that we can't. All that we can reasonably expect to do with a microscope is to obtain a *total count* of living *and* dead cells. In order to count living cells only we must measure directly the ability to multiply. This is the basis of a *viable count* which is normally done by dispersing a known volume of a cell suspension (diluted if necessary) onto a plate of a suitable growth medium; after incubation, one colony will be produced from one viable organism. Viable counts done in this way are by far the most sensitive method of determining growth or multiplication since most others require at least a million cells to measure with any accuracy. Unfortunately viable counts are tedious to do and for many purposes may be unnecessary.

A variety of methods have been employed to measure growth as distinct from multiplication such as determination of the dry weight, the amount of a typical cell component, the volume of packed cells or their catalytic power. The method actually adopted depends upon the purpose of the experiment. If rapidity is the primary consideration, by far the best is to measure turbidity either by the light scattering directly in a nephelometer or indirectly with a spectrophotometer.

## THE BATCH CULTURE OF MICROORGANISMS

Let us consider what happens when growth is measured after inoculation of a small number of suitable microorganisms into a sterile liquid medium. A typical growth curve is given in Fig. 4.2; four main phases can be recognised.

(1) *The lag phase*. This period in which no multiplication occurs represents a time when the inoculum cells are adapting themselves to active growth in the new environment. The length of the phase varies widely, but it will be long if the inoculum cells are old, are damaged in any way or if they have been grown previously in a quite different medium. If the inoculum is of rapidly growing cells from an identical medium then the lag will be hardly perceptible.

(2) *The exponential phase*. Here the cells are growing at a constant rate, that is the generation time (the time between divisions) is constant. In a unicellular microrganism, the result of such a constant *rate* of growth must be an exponential increase in the mass and number of cells (see Fig. 4.3). This phase used to be known as the log phase but it is now more fashionable to call it the exponential phase. The consequence of it is that although the increase in cell number is slow initially, it eventually becomes explosive and the practical effects of such growth in nature are many. For example, once a bacterial infection is properly established in the body, any means of combating it must be increasingly

48

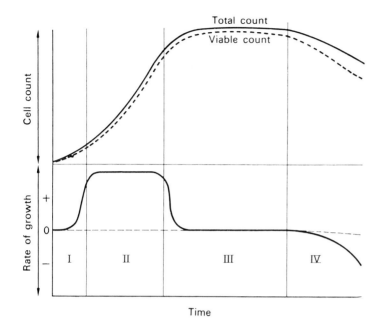

**Figure 4.2** The batch growth curve. The top section represents the cell count and the bottom section the rate of growth. I, lag phase; II, exponential (log) phase; III, stationary phase; IV, death phase

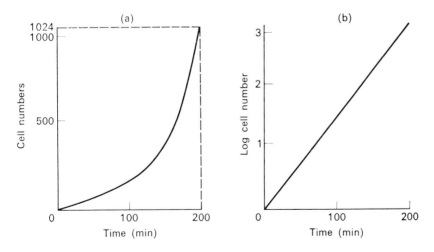

**Figure 4.3** The multiplication of a unicellular microorganism with a generation time of 20 minutes. A straight line is obtained with a semi-log plot (b)

efficient. The actual rate of exponential growth varies widely, some bacteria at high temperatures having a generation time as small as 10 minutes while in some eukaryotic microorganisms it may be as high as 24 hours. However, this exponential phase cannot go on indefinitely. Consider again the case of a typical bacterium with a volume of 1 $\mu m^3$ growing with a generation time of 20 minutes. Figure 4.3 shows that after $3\frac{1}{3}$ hours (200 minutes) the cell number has increased by a factor of 1024. For the sake of convenience, let us round this figure to a thousand-fold increase. This means that as long as exponential growth continues, there will be a further thousand-fold increase every $3\frac{1}{3}$ hours with the results presented below.

| Time (hr) | No. of cells | Volume of cells |
|---|---|---|
| 0 | 1 | 1 $\mu m^3$ |
| $3\frac{1}{3}$ | $10^3$ | |
| $6\frac{2}{3}$ | $10^6$ | |
| 10 | $10^9$ | 1 $mm^3$ |
| 20 | $10^{18}$ | 1 $m^3$ |
| 30 | $10^{27}$ | 1 $km^3$ |
| 40 | $10^{36}$ | 1,000 $km^3$ |
| 50 | $10^{45}$ | 1,000,000 $km^3$ |

After 50 hours' incubation the volume of cells would be greater than that of the whole earth, thus illustrating the potential of exponential growth. Clearly such results cannot occur in practice and growth must be circumscribed. Normally the limiting factor is lack of food or, more accurately, lack of one particular essential nutrient that becomes completely exhausted in the culture medium. As soon as this happens, growth ceases and the cells go into the stationary phase. Another reason for the termination of the exponential phase may be the accumulation of toxic end products of metabolism. For example many yeasts produce ethanol as a result of fermentation and as soon as a level of about 10% is reached, growth ceases and the cells may die. A practical consequence is that wines cannot be prepared with an alcohol content much above 14% and to increase this value a distillation stage has to be introduced. Until the stationary phase is brought on by an insufficiency of nutrients or the accumulation of toxic products, there should be no population density above which growth is inhibited except for factors such as availability of oxygen or, in the case of photosynthetic microorganisms, the lack of light penetration.

(3) *The stationary phase.* In this phase the number of cells remains constant. Although the stationary phase can result from an equilibrium between multiplication and death and this may occur if toxic products accumulate, normally it is the consequence of neither growth nor death. In other words, the cells remain in a state of suspended animation. The length of the stationary phase depends upon the factor bringing it on and upon the microorganism concerned and may be minutes, hours, days or even weeks.

(4) *The death phase*. In this phase the cells begin to die and as a result there is an increasing divergence between the total and viable counts (Fig. 4.2). However, when the irreversible process of death occurs, cells commonly start to digest themselves and lysis or, more strictly speaking, *autolysis* results. Such autolysis has some interesting results. If a laboratory culture is allowed to go into the death phase so that a reasonable percentage of cells lyse, those remaining may be able to grow on the products of this lysis. In other words, cannibalism occurs. This short growth phase is followed by a further death phase and the process is repeated until no cells remain. In this way a culture may remain viable for a very long time although it should be noted that we are eventually selecting those organisms in a culture that lyse less readily or are the best cannibals (see p. 84).

## THE CONTINUOUS CULTURE OF MICROORGANISMS

So far we have been considering the batch culture of microorganisms. Growth occurs in a vessel of finite dimensions and eventually ceases. Is it not possible to devise an apparatus in which the cells are kept growing indefinitely by the continuous addition of fresh nutrient medium and the continuous removal of grown cells and their products? Surprisingly enough, work on these lines was not initiated until the 1940's and even then the significance of the pioneer work took some time to penetrate. Indeed much of the development was the result of work on more efficient ways of producing cells for biological warfare (or, as we are usually told, for defence against biological warfare).

The method of growth was called continuous culture and the apparatus most commonly used was the chemostat, a simple form of which is illustrated in Fig. 4.4. Fresh sterile medium is pumped into the growth vessel at a steady rate while a constant level device removes cells and their products at an equal rate. A stirrer homogenises the fresh medium with the culture and normally also acts as an aeration device. The apparatus can be elaborated further by devices for sampling, pH control, temperature control, antifoam addition and so on. The rate of growth in a chemostat is regulated by the rate of addition of fresh medium while the constituents of this medium can also be altered to produce different steady-state levels of nutrients. Although batch culture is the most common method for the growth of microorganisms both in the laboratory and in industry, continuous culture has some real advantages, some of which are summarised below.

(1) Reproducible cells are obtainable from one day to another once a steady-state has been reached. This is not easy to achieve with the rapidly changing environment of a batch culture, a fact not always sufficiently recognised by microbiologists.

(2) A continuous culture system, once set up, can run for months provided either the entry of contaminants is prevented by aseptic conditions or the growth of any contaminant is rendered unlikely by the environmental conditions employed. This advantage together with the relatively small size of fermentor required compared with that to produce an equivalent number of

cells in a batch culture system, has led to more efficient industrial processes for the growth of microorganisms or the manufacture of many of their products.

(3) The method may be nearer to that of microbial growth in Nature. For example, the rumen is a good example of a continuous culture system (p. 93). However, it is probably fair to say that general microbial growth in Nature has certain elements of continuous and batch culture. Thus the growth of bacteria

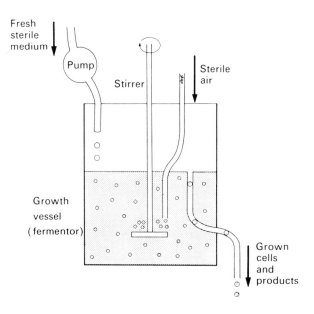

Figure 4.4 An apparatus for the continuous growth of an aerobic microorganism. Although not shown, the growth vessel normally contains means to maintain a constant temperature and pH and to prevent foaming

in the human intestine may correspond more nearly to a batch or a continuous system depending on the frequency of feeding, the variety of food and the constancy of defaecation. In general, each natural ecosystem should be analysed for its own particular set of circumstances and it is dangerous to simplify the systems into analogy with either batch or continuous growth. A pond is a pond is a pond.

## SYNCHRONOUS GROWTH

A growing microbial culture normally contains cells dividing asynchronously but there has been a recent and increasing interest in the phases of the cell cycle, that is what happens between one cell division and the next. However, it is difficult to apply standard biochemical techniques to a unit as small as a single microbial cell and it is necessary to amplify the physiological events by producing a synchronously dividing culture in which all the cells divide at roughly the same time. Two general methods of producing synchronous cultures are available.

(1) *Phasing methods*. These methods rely on synchronising an exponential-phase culture by appropriate and usually sudden changes in the environment such as alteration in temperature, level of nutrients or illumination.

(2) *Selection methods* in which there is a physical separation of cells from an exponential-phase culture at a particular point in the growth cycle. For example, centrifugation on a density gradient can separate the smallest cells from a culture and it can be assumed that these have all just divided. Other methods depend on filtration or on the selective adsorption of cells on surfaces. These selection methods are preferable to those involving phasing as they are less subject to the objection that the process of synchronisation causes an extensive metabolic disturbance within the cells and hence produces abnormal results.

## THE REQUIREMENTS FOR MICROBIAL GROWTH

We have seen that microbial growth can be very rapid. However, in order to maintain such a high rate of growth, various parameters in the physical and the chemical nature of the environment must be carefully controlled and it is very important to understand them. First, the environment must contain suitable nutrients from which the microorganisms obtain their raw materials and energy; these will be dealt with in Chapter 7. Second, the physicochemical conditions must be suitable and must now be considered.

### Water

Water makes up about 80% of the weight of a microbial cell and is clearly essential if only as a nutrient. Furthermore, most microorganisms obtain their food in a soluble form although some eukaryotes are able to extract the water they need directly from the air as do those responsible for the biodeterioration of natural materials such as cellulose, wool or leather in the tropics. However, if dried food is kept away from moist air it should stay unspoilt for long periods of time, a fact made use of as a means of preservation.

It is important to realise that the environmental conditions for growth are not necessarily the same as those for survival. Thus many microorganisms can *survive* drying especially if this drying occurs at low temperatures. For example, microbes are preserved by freeze-drying (*lyophilisation*) a process in which a cell suspension is frozen rapidly and dried by sublimation of the water under a high vacuum. Once the organism has survived drying, it will remain, viable in this state for very long periods of time.

### Temperature

One of the most important factors affecting the rate of microbial growth is the environmental temperature. As shown in Fig. 4.5, there is a minimum figure

53

below which growth will not occur; as we rise above this temperature the rate of growth increases in accordance with normal laws governing the effect of temperature on the chemical reactions, mainly enzyme-catalysed, that make up growth. However, a point is reached when there is also a very rapid increase in the rate of inactivation of heat-sensitive cell components such as enzymes, ribosomes, DNA and membranes. Above an optimum temperature, this heat denaturation will occur so rapidly that there is a correspondingly rapid drop in the rate of growth to a maximum temperature.

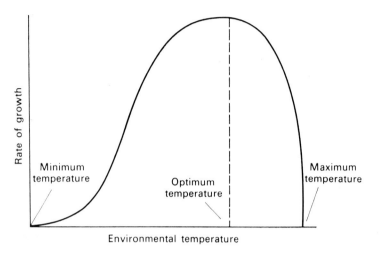

**Figure 4.5** The effect of temperature on the rate of growth of a microorganism

Most microorganisms have a temperature range of 20–30° within which growth will occur. It appears that the whole structure, metabolic machinery and control systems in a cell are such as to allow proper functioning only within such a range although the actual value of the minimum, optimum and maximum growth temperatures varies considerably. Most microorganisms have an optimum between 20° and 40° and are called *mesophilic*. However, those inhabiting cold environments such as polar areas can grow at much lower temperatures and large numbers of microorganisms are found on the surface of such unpromising areas as glaciers where they may even cause a visible green or red colour. Organisms like these are called *psychrophilic* and may cause trouble in food stored in refrigerators over a long period although fortunately they do not produce dangerous toxins. Other microorganisms called *thermophilic* are able to inhabit environments such as hot springs or compost heaps. These fascinating creatures can grow at temperatures as high as 80–90° when the great majority of living organisms would die rapidly. We do not completely understand how they do it since the problem is much greater for an actively growing cell than a spore where the essential elements of the cell are held in a state of suspended animation. The answer probably lies in a dual effect of an

54

increased stability of many of the components of the cell coupled with more active repair mechanisms on heat-denatured components.

Again a distinction must be drawn between growth and survival. Although most microorganisms are rapidly killed above their maximum growth temperature, they are not necessarily killed below their minimum growth temperature. Indeed, the ability of most bacteria to survive at liquid-nitrogen temperatures is the basis of what is becoming one of the most popular methods for preserving microorganisms—a suspension is simply placed in an ultra-low-temperature cabinet.

## pH

As with temperature, the pH range at which a microorganism will grow varies considerably although for a given species it usually covers about 4 pH units. Most organisms grow best at pH near neutrality, bacteria usually slightly on the alkaline side and algae and fungi on the acid side. However, some microbes can grow at exceptionally high or low pH values. For example, a few bacteria that obtain their energy by the oxidation of inorganic sulphur compounds to sulphuric acid can grow at a pH value as low as 0 (i.e. $IN$-$H_2SO_4$). Other bacteria causing infections of the human urinary tract can hydrolyse urea and this leads to the production of an excess of ammonia with a consequent rise of pH; these organisms grow at pH values as high as 11.

The inability of most bacteria to grow below a pH value of 3–4 is made use of in the food industry where pickling is a common method of preservation. Acetic acid in the form of vinegar may be added to the food or bacteria may themselves lower the pH value by fermentation.

## Oxygen and redox potential

The presence or absence of oxygen divides organisms into three main classes (Table 4.1). The basis of this differentiation is mainly in the nature of the energy-producing systems and can be summarised as follows:

(1) Some microorganisms require oxygen as a terminal electron acceptor for oxidation (see p. 62) and if this is the only means of energy production, the organism will be a *strict aerobe*. A similar result will occur if the degradation of some carbon and energy growth substrates such as hydrocarbons requires the entry of an oxygen atom or atoms into the molecule.

Table 4.1.  The effect of oxygen on the growth of microorganisms

|  | Growth in | | |
|---|---|---|---|
|  | Air | Low $O_2$ | Absence of $O_2$ |
| Strict aerobe | ++++ | + | — |
| Facultative anaerobe | ++++ (or ++) | ++ | ++ |
| Strict anaerobe | — | — | ++ |

(2) If, in addition, a microorganism can obtain its energy in the absence of oxygen, it will be a *facultative anaerobe*. In this case, growth is usually more abundant aerobically than anaerobically.

(3) *Strict anaerobes* have an energy-producing system which does not require oxygen, and in addition, they are actually poisoned by oxygen.

As would be expected, the aerobic or anaerobic nature of a microorganism is related to the normal natural environment of that organism. Thus methane-producing microorganisms are strict anaerobes and live in an environment such as the lower gut of animals. On the other hand, methane-utilising bacteria are strict aerobes and must occur in environments where oxygen is available from the air but also supplemented by methane as the result of the action of methane-producing bacteria in related anaerobic areas. As a result, in soil we find methane-producers in the lower layers and methane-utilisers in the top layers.

## Osmotic pressure

Most microbes are capable of growing within a fairly wide range of environmental osmotic pressure. Their ability to survive osmotic pressures lower than those of their cytoplasms and thus to avoid lysis is related either to the presence of a mechanically-tough cell wall or to a water-excreting mechanism such as a contractile vacuole. However, there are limits to the upper level of osmotic tolerance and the colonisation of such environments as salt lakes, salt pans and, to a lesser extent, the oceans requires specialised organisms called *osmophiles* or *halophiles*. Fortunately most microorganisms are unable to grow at such high osmotic pressures and this fact is made use of in the preservation of food by salting or by the addition of sugar.

## Hydrostatic pressure

The only natural environments with hydrostatic pressures high enough to inhibit the growth of most microorganisms are the depths of the oceans. Here pressures may be as high as a thousand times those on the surface and we find colonisation by specialised *barophiles*. Little is known about them since they will not grow at normal atmospheric pressures and special apparatus is required for their collection, isolation and study.

## Radiation

Most microorganisms are killed by high doses of electromagnetic radiation particularly in the ultraviolet range and by smaller doses of ionising radiation. Death occurs mainly by damage to DNA and variation in resistance usually reflects differing abilities of cells to repair their radiation-damaged DNA.

Visible light is essential to the growth of photosynthetic microorganisms since it provides their energy source and these organisms usually have special mechanisms to avoid the deleterious effects of such radiation.

56

# GENERAL CONSIDERATIONS

What conclusions can be made about the effect of the physicochemical environment of microbial growth? Three over-all groups of principles emerge.

(1) A microbial species generally has a fairly wide range of environmental conditions in which it will grow. This range is usually higher in prokaryotes than eukaryotes as it is in microorganisms compared with the cells of higher animals and plants. The width of this range can reflect either a less-sensitive cellular mechanism or a capacity for controlling the cell in presence of environmental extremes, in other words, for homeostasis. Both explanations can hold. Thus the ability to withstand a wide temperature range must be due to a difference in cell sensitivity while growth at different pH values may generally relate to the capability of regulating the internal pH of the cytoplasm so that it remains near neutrality.

(2) The microbial kingdom as a whole shows an extraordinary ability to occupy extreme environmental niches. Yet again this ability is particularly marked in prokaryotes. For example, an extreme environment such as the Dead Sea or near the source of a hot spring will be populated by prokaryotes almost to the exclusion of eukaryotes. The advantages of the colonisation of these extreme environments will be the lack of competition from other species for the available nutrients. Presumably the simpler structure of the prokaryotic cell is more capable of evolutionary adaptation or the genetic mechanisms are themselves more capable of change. On the other hand the eukaryotic cell is more suited to evolutionary change in the direction of a multicellular differentiated form of life.

The ability of prokaryotes to adapt themselves both phenotypically and genotypically to environmental changes is important in their use for fundamental biological research. It has permitted an understanding of the cellular control mechanisms and has allowed a researcher to choose an organism having a particular property well developed and thus suited to his needs. Thus if you wish to study the mechanism of DNA repair, it is logical to look at an organism in which this is developed to its highest degree and these organisms are generally prokaryotes.

(3) Finally, a study of the effect of the environment on microbial growth is of immense value to the food manufacturer. We have seen that a variety of extremes can be and are used in food preservation; a choice of their relative merits depends on the particular food under consideration.

# THE GROWTH OF VIRUSES

The mode of virus growth and multiplication is quite different to that of cells and since it is easier to understand in relationship to the biosynthetic machinery of the host cell, it will be considered separately in Chapter 6.

# 5 The metabolism and nutrition of microorganisms

One of the most important characteristics of microorganisms is their high rate of growth. Many have a generation time of under 30 minutes and this implies the ability to synthesise their own weight of cell material in this period. In order to do so, they must have a correspondingly high rate of metabolism. Indeed, there tends to be an inverse relationship between the rates of metabolism or growth and the size of a living organism. For example, if we take the rate of oxygen uptake per unit mass as a measure of energy production in an aerobic organism and if the figure for man is taken as unity, the following levels can be obtained:

| Elephant | Man | Mouse | Microorganism | |
|----------|-----|-------|---------------|----------|
| | | | Eukaryotic | Prokaryotic |
| 0·2 | 1·0 | 10 | 100 | 1,000 |

How is this high rate of microbial metabolism maintained? One of the main limiting factors is the rate of uptake of nutrients and removal of waste products, processes both occurring at the cell surface. The smaller the organism, the greater will be the ratio of its surface area to its volume or to its weight and hence the easier it will be for it to have a high rate of metabolism and growth. This is illustrated by two examples:

(a) A 220 lb man

$$\frac{\text{Surface area}}{\text{Weight}} = \frac{24,000 \text{ cm}^2}{10,000 \text{ g}} = 2\cdot4 \text{ cm}^2/\text{g}$$

(b) A typical bacterium

$$\frac{\text{Surface area}}{\text{Weight}} = \frac{1 \times 10^{-7}\text{cm}^2}{2 \times 10^{-12} \text{ g}} = 50,000 \text{ cm}^2/\text{g}$$

Of course, higher organisms have developed special mechanisms to increase their useful surface area such as intestines, lungs, kidneys and circulating blood-streams. However, microorganisms gain a considerable advantage from their small size and may actually increase their surface area still further by invagination of the cytoplasmic membrane (p. 15).

If this chapter had been written in the 1940's, it would have to have been admitted that very little was known about microbial metabolism. An exception was the use of yeasts for early studies on the glycolytic pathway and the electron-transport system, but bacterial metabolism was largely an unexplored field. Why was this? One reason was that in those days most microbiologists didn't know any biochemistry and most biochemists didn't know any microbiology. Yeasts, on the other hand, could be bought from the local brewery or bakery. Another reason was the difficulty in preparing cell-free extracts of bacteria because of their small size and their tough cell wall and little real study of metabolic pathways is possible with intact cells. Gradually the atmosphere has changed. Training in biology has become less parochial and several methods of breaking microbial cells without too much denaturation (loss in biological activity) of the contents have been developed. Biologists have come to realise that microorganisms are ideal for the study of some of the basic principles of biochemistry and molecular biology. Indeed, we know more about the biochemistry of one bacterium—*Escherichia coli*—than we do about any other living organism.

## THE CHEMICAL COMPOSITION OF MICROORGANISMS

Before we consider microbial metabolism it is essential to mention the end product of this metabolism, that is the chemical components which make up the microbial cell. Typical figures are shown in Table 5.1. At the same time,

Table 5.1.   The main components of typical microbial cells (figures as % of dry weight)

| | Protein | Nucleic acid | Polysaccharide | Lipid | Peptidoglycan | Others |
|---|---|---|---|---|---|---|
| Prokaryote | 50 | 10 | 10 | 10 | 10 | 10 |
| Eukaryote | 50 | 5 | 15 | 15 | — | 15 |
| Monomer components of polymers | Amino acids | Nucleo-tides | Mono-saccharides | — | Amino acids Mono-saccharides | — |

it must be realised that there are wide variations in chemical composition both between different groups of microorganisms and between the same organism grown under different environmental conditions. A few examples of such variations are given below.

(a) In all microorganisms, the RNA content increases with growth rate (p. 17). Consequently, since prokaryotes in general grow faster than eukaryotes, this fact is reflected in their high levels of RNA.

(b) Gram-negative bacteria have more lipid and less mucopeptide than gram-positives because of their different cell walls (p. 18).

(c) Cells grown in presence of an excess of a carbon and energy source tend to have a high content of storage polymers such as lipid and polysaccharide (p. 18).

If we look at Table 5.1 it can be seen that 70–80% of the cell dry weight is made up of macromolecular polymers, the remainder being in the form of lipid and low-molecular weight substances such as metabolites, coenzymes and inorganic ions. One important fact to recognise is the invariability of most of these compounds in living organisms. The amino acids in proteins, the nucleotides in nucleic acids, many types of lipids and most coenzymes are of universal occurrence. Although there are considerable differences in the means employed by cells to obtain their energy and building blocks for growth and in the range of their biosynthetic ability, there tends to be a unity in the actual mechanisms of biosynthesis and in the final product in terms of cell composition.

The metabolism of a cell, then, must be directed to the synthesis of the following compounds:

20 L-amino acids
2-4 Peptidoglycan amino acids (in prokaryotes only)
5 Purines and Pyrimidines
c.10 Monosaccharides

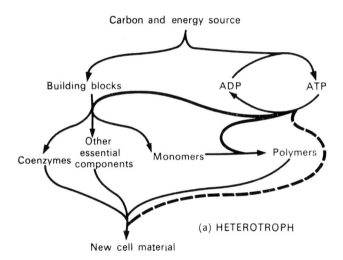

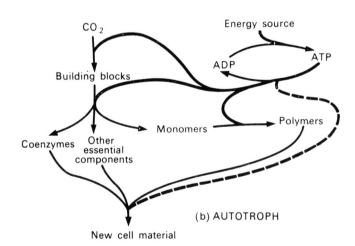

**Figure 5.1** The major steps in the metabolism of (a) heterotrophs and (b) autotrophs

c.10 Lipids

c.20 Coenzymes

A variety of other essential components

The minimum number of organic compounds that must be either synthesised by the cell or provided in the environment as monomers or as cell constituents in their own right is probably between 100 and 200. In most microorganisms, the majority of these constituents can be synthesised by the organism itself, the stages of this metabolism being as follows:

(1) The provision of energy by the formation of ATP from ADP (or from AMP although for simplicity only ADP will be mentioned in this book).

(2) The provision of basic building blocks from the external carbon source or sources. It is at this level that all living organisms are commonly divided into two major groupings—the heterotrophs and the autotrophs. In *heterotrophs* the sources of carbon and energy are the same substances; they are broken down partly to provide energy and partly to supply building blocks. In *autotrophs* the energy source is not provided by a catabolic metabolism of organic substances and is different from the carbon source which is usually carbon dioxide. Although this distinction is clear enough for plants (autotrophs), for animals (heterotrophs) and for many microorganisms (either autotrophs or heterotrophs), there are other microorganisms which make the borderline somewhat blurred. Some are capable of either an autotrophic or a heterotrophic existence (*facultative autotrophs*) while others have some characteristics of each group.

(3) The conversion of these building blocks into the monomers, coenzymes and other cell components noted above.

(4) The polymerisation of these monomers.

(5) The formation of the quaternary structure of the polymers, together with other essential components, and their movement to the appropriate part of the cell where they form the structures necessary for their normal functioning.

These processes are summarised in Fig. 5.1.

Let us consider metabolism in these stages, emphasising the variation that occurs amongst microorganisms.

## THE PRODUCTION OF ENERGY

### Heterotrophs

The majority of microorganisms are heterotrophs obtaining their energy by two general phosphorylation mechanisms during the chemical breakdown of the organic carbon and energy source or sources provided in the environment. In *substrate-level phosphorylation* the organic substance undergoes an exergonic reaction in such a way that part of the energy released provides a high-energy phosphate bond attached to the substrate which is subsequently transferred onto ADP to give ATP. In *oxidative phosphorylation* an electron donor ($AH_2$) is oxidised and the electrons (usually in pairs) so produced pass through an electron-transport system to a terminal electron acceptor (B) in such a way that the energy released is partly utilised to produce ATP from ADP i.e.

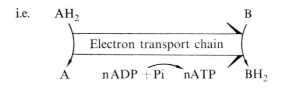

or $AH_2 + B + nADP + nPi \longrightarrow A + BH_2 + nATP$

The value of n, which represents the number of energy-rich phosphate bonds produced in the passage of a pair of electrons through the electron-transport system, may be 1, 2 or 3. The figure depends partly on the energy released in the oxidation of $AH_2$ at the expense of B and therefore on the difference in the redox potential of the $AH_2 \leftrightarrows A$ system and the $B \leftrightarrows BH_2$ system. The greater this difference, then the more ATP that can theoretically be produced.

Three general methods exist by which a carbon and energy source can be broken down to provide energy.

(1) *Aerobic Respiration.* In aerobic respiration, the carbon and energy source is broken down by a series of reactions, the oxidation stages occurring at the expense of oxygen as the terminal electron acceptor.

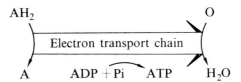

By far the greater amount of useful energy produced during aerobic respiration comes from oxidative phosphorylation although the complexity of the electron transport system varies amongst different microorganism. Thus yeasts can have a series of carriers in their mitochondria very similar to those of higher animals, while bacteria often have fewer cytochromes and the simplicity of their electron transport systems can in some instances be reflected in a smaller number of phosphorylation stages. In the classical example of the complete oxidation of glucose to carbon dioxide, the usual pathway appears to be common to microbes, plants and animals; glucose is first converted by the glycolytic pathway to pyruvic acid which is then oxidised to carbon dioxide by the tricarboxylic acid cycle, the major part of the ATP formed being by oxidative phosphorylation. Assuming three energy-rich phosphate bonds are formed during each passage through the electron-transport chain, the over-all oxidation can be explained as follows:

$$C_6H_{12}O_6 + 6\ O_2 + 38\ ADP + 38\ Pi \rightarrow 6\ CO_2 + 6\ H_2O + 38\ ATP$$

Although carbon dioxide is the commonest end product of the oxidation of a carbon energy source, some microorganisms carry out only a partial oxidation. For example, some fungi produce oxalic acid

$$C_6H_{12}O_6 + 4.5\ O_2 \rightarrow 3\ (COOH)_2 + 3\ H_2O$$

(2) *Anaerobic respiration.* Although oxygen is the most common and efficient electron acceptor, some prokaryotes are able to utilise certain inorganic electron acceptors by a process confusingly called anaerobic respiration. Thus nitrate is reduced to ammonia, nitrous oxide or molecular nitrogen; sulphate is reduced to sulphide and carbon dioxide is reduced to methane, i.e.

The following points should be noted:

(a) The pathways for the breakdown of a carbon and energy source in aerobic and anaerobic respiration are identical. The only difference resides in the fate of the electrons produced in the oxidation steps.

(b) The amount of ATP formed in the passage of two electrons through the electron transport chain depends on the difference in redox potential between the electron donor and the electron acceptor. Since these inorganic electron acceptors have higher redox potentials than oxygen, less ATP will usually be produced in anaerobic compared with aerobic respiration.

(c) Anaerobic respiration plays an important part in maintaining the cycle of elements in a natural environment (see Chapter 9).

(3) *Fermentation.* In fermentation no external electron acceptor is required. Instead the carbon and energy source is broken down by a series of reactions which release energy by substrate-level phosphorylation. Although oxido-reductions occur, they must be balanced so that the average state of oxidation of the products is the same as the substrate.

Consider the fermentation of glucose. Most microorganisms employ the glycolytic pathway for the initial attack with the resultant production of pyruvic acid

i.e. $C_6H_{12}O_6 + 2\ PN + 2\ ADP + 2\ Pi \rightarrow 2\ CH_3CO.COOH + 2\ PNH_2 + 2\ ATP$
(where $PN + PNH_2$ are the oxidised and reduced forms of pyridine nucleotide).

For fermentation to continue, the reduced pyridine nucleotide (normally $NADH_2$) must be reoxidised, a process that may or may not produce additional useful energy.

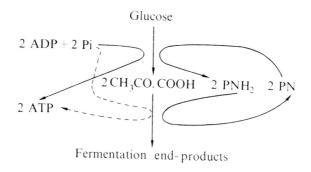

Glucose

2 ADP + 2 Pi

2 CH₃CO.COOH    2 PNH₂    2 PN

2 ATP

Fermentation end-products

There is a wide range of fermentation end-products and only two will be mentioned here. The lactic acid bacteria reduce pyruvic acid directly to lactic acid.

$$2\ CH_3CO.COOH + 2\ PNH_2 \rightarrow 2\ CH_3CHOH.COOH + 2\ PN$$

The end result is as follows:

$$C_6H_{12}O_6 + 2\ ADP + 2\ Pi \rightarrow 2\ CH_3CHOH.COOH + 2\ ATP$$

Yeasts carry out the slightly more complex alcoholic fermentation,

$$i.e.\quad 2\ CH_3CO.COOH \rightarrow 2\ CH_3CHO + 2\ CO_2$$
$$2\ CH_3CHO + 2\ PNH_2 \rightarrow 2\ CH_3CH_2OH + 2\ PN$$

The end result is the formation of ethanol and carbon dioxide.

$$C_6H_{12}O_6 + 2\ ADP + 2\ Pi \rightarrow 2\ CH_3CH_2OH + 2\ CO_2 + 2\ ATP$$

These are only two of the many end-products of fermentation in micro-organisms. The nature of these end-products is often an important factor in classification and many are also of great industrial value. Anaerobic growth by fermentation is much less efficient energetically than aerobic respiration, the yield of cells from a unit amount of glucose usually being about a tenth. This is less than the difference in the ATP yield per molecule of glucose oxidised or fermented (see above) since a higher percentage of glucose will be assimilated to cell material in aerobic growth compared to anaerobic growth.

## Autotrophs

Autotrophs fall into two groups according to their mode of energy production.

(1) *Chemoautotrophs.* These bacteria obtain their energy by the oxidation of inorganic substrates usually at the expense of oxygen as the terminal electron acceptor. ATP is formed by oxidative phosphorylation and the basic difference from energy production in aerobic heterotrophs is that the electron donor happens to be inorganic. Some examples of these intriguing organisms are shown in Table 5.2.

**Table 5.2.** The electron donors and their products in the energy-producing reactions of some chemoautotrophic bacteria.

| | Electron donor and product |
|---|---|
| Nitrifying bacteria | $\begin{cases} NH_3 \longrightarrow NO_2 \\ NO_2 \longrightarrow NO_3 \end{cases}$ |
| Sulphur bacteria | $\begin{cases} H_2S \longrightarrow S \\ S \longrightarrow SO_4{}^{2-} \end{cases}$ |
| Hydrogen bacteria | $H_2 \longrightarrow H_2O$ |
| Methane bacteria | $CH_4 \longrightarrow CO_2$ |
| Iron bacteria | $Fe^{2+} \longrightarrow Fe^{3+}$ |

The chemoautotrophs are an important group from an economic point of view. One of them has also become something of a 'cause célèbre'. *Thiobacillus thiooxidans* was used to test the idea of the unity of general biochemical principles since it was considered to be as bizarre a living organism as existed. It gets its carbon from $CO_2$, its energy by oxidising inorganic sulphur compounds to sulphuric acid, it will grow at a pH below 1·0 and it cannot grow on normal organic substrates such as glucose which may actually be inhibitory. However, we have seen that there is nothing unusual in the actual mechanism of ATP production; the electron donor for oxidative phosphorylation just happens to be an inorganic sulphur compound. The intermediary metabolism of the organism is little different from that of any other autotroph which uses $CO_2$ as the sole carbon source. Unfortunately for the scientist but fortunately for the student, we will probably have to visit faraway planets before we can find a really unusual biochemistry although even here there are some biochemists who believe that organisms similar to ours would have evolved inevitably.

(2) *Photoautotrophs.* The photoautotrophs obtain their energy mainly by photosynthetic phosphorylation, a process involving the excitation of chlorophyll molecules by light so that high-energy electrons are emitted thereby causing the reduction of special compounds of low redox potential. These reduced substances can then be oxidised through an electron-transport system with the concomitant production of ATP by a process analogous to that of oxidative phosphorylation; as a result the electron is returned to the chlorophyll molecule. Although there is still uncertainty about the actual carriers involved, this process of *cyclic photophosphorylation* is probably similar in all photoautotrophs (Fig. 5.2). However, they differ in the nature of their photosynthetic pigments (chlorophylls and carotenoids) and in certain features of the process of *non-cyclic photophosphorylation* whereby the reduced compound of low redox potential produced by the action of the excited electron from chlorophyll is used to reduce pyridine nucleotide through an abbreviated electron-transport chain. Electrons are returned to chlorophyll by an external electron donor and it is here that there is a major difference in the photosynthetic mechanisms of bacteria and those of algae and green plants. In the latter case, water acts as the electron donor and oxygen is evolved while in the former group some other external electron donor ($AH_2$) such as inorganic sulphur compounds,

organic substances or molecular hydrogen must be supplied. Consequently no oxygen is evolved (see Fig. 5.2). It should be noted that non-cyclic photophosphorylation produces reduced pyridine nucleotide in addition to ATP, an important property when carbon dioxide assimilation is considered (see p. 67).

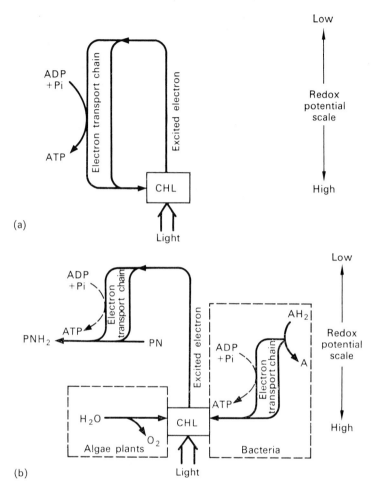

**Figure 5.2** A simplified scheme for (a) cyclic and (b) non-cyclic photophosphorylation. CHL, Chlorophyll

Clearly microorganisms exhibit a wide range of different methods to obtain their energy, a range that reflects the large number of different environmental situations that they have been able to colonise.

## THE PROVISION OF BASIC BUILDING BLOCKS

In heterotrophs the carbon and energy source is catabolised by a series of reactions to provide a group of essential metabolites which are used as the basic building blocks for the synthesis of the 100–200 monomers, coenzymes and essential structural units of the cell. These basic or central intermediary metabolites are compounds like sugar phosphates, pyruvate, phosphoglycerate, acetate, oxalacetate, succinate, and α-ketoglutarate. The enzymes catalysing these interconversions such as those of the glycolytic pathway and the tricarboxylic acid cycle are generally common to all cellular life and are produced irrespective of the environmental conditions; we will refer to them collectively as constituting the *basal intermediary metabolism*. An important function of these enzymes is that they are concerned in heterotrophs both with the production of energy and with the synthesis of the essential cell building blocks. In autotrophs, since carbon dioxide is the carbon source for growth they usually function as anabolic or biosynthetic enzymes. Such enzymes and pathways which can function in both catabolism and anabolism are known as *amphibolic* and they are usually present irrespective of the environmental conditions. In other words, they are

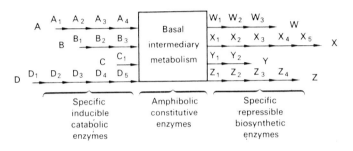

Figure 5.3 A diagrammatic representation of the enzymes concerned in the conversion of carbon and energy sources (A,B,C,D) into the monomers and coenzymes (W,X,Y,Z) required for growth

*constitutive.* Leading into these basal pathways are the enzymes concerned in the *specific* utilisation of a carbon and energy source. Since many heterotrophic microorganisms are capable of using over a hundred different carbon and energy sources and since many specific enzymes may be involved in each of the pathways, a cell may have the *potential* to produce a very large number of catabolic enzymes. In general such enzymes are only formed when they are actually required, that is when the specific carbon and energy source is present in the environment. They are called *inducible enzymes* and their synthesis requires the presence of an inducer which is usually the particular carbon and energy source. An example is the induction of the enzyme α-glucosidase (maltase) by the inducer maltose. As a result, maltose is hydrolysed to glucose which can be broken down by constitutive enzymes. In the general scheme presented in Fig. 5.3, A acts as an inducer for the biosynthesis of enzymes $A_1$, $A_2$, $A_3$ and $A_4$, B for enzymes $B_1$, $B_2$ and $B_3$ and so on.

In autotrophs, $CO_2$ is the source of carbon. It is converted into the basal intermediary metabolic system by a series of reactions (the Calvin cycle) which seem to be generally common to all such organisms, be they chemoautotrophs or photoautotrophs. This conversion requires energy in the form of ATP and reducing power in the form of ATP and reduced pyridine nucleotide.

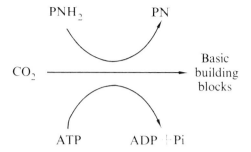

The mechanism for ATP synthesis in autotrophs has been discussed earlier in this chapter as has that for the production of reduced pyridine nucleotide by photosynthesis (p. 66). In chemoautotrophs, the electrons necessary for the reduction of pyridine nucleotide are provided by the inorganic electron donor which also acts as the energy source.

## THE BIOSYNTHESIS OF MONOMERS AND COENZYMES

Leading from the basal intermediary metabolic systems are a series of specific pathways concerned in the biosynthesis of the monomers, coenzymes and other essential compounds needed for growth. There is a considerable variation amongst microorganisms in the range of biosynthetic pathways present. While some have a complete set and can synthesise all their organic components for themselves, others have a restricted range of biosynthetic ability. These differences are reflected in the nutrients required for growth (see p. 70). If a microorganism is growing in an environment containing the end-product of a biosynthetic pathway (say compound W in Fig. 5.3), it is clearly advantageous to the economy of the cell that W be no longer synthesised and therefore that enzymes $W_1$, $W_2$ and $W_3$ be no longer active and, preferably, no longer formed. Two methods are used to bring about this result.

(1) W inhibits the first enzyme in its specific biosynthesis ($W_1$)—the process of *feedback inhibition*.

(2) W inhibits the biosynthesis of all the enzymes concerned in its specific biosynthesis (i.e. $W_1$, $W_2$ and $W_3$). Such enzymes are called repressible enzymes and the process is called *repression*. Control mechanisms like repression and induction are particularly important in microorganisms in their struggle for existence where even the slightest increase in the growth rate may lead to dominance in a particular environment.

The essential monomers must eventually be produced in an activated form so that no additional energy source is required for their polymerisation. These activated monomers (e.g. amino acyl-RNA, nucleoside diphosphate sugars, nucleoside triphosphates etc.) are usually the same in microorganisms as in higher organisms.

# POLYMERISATION

In general, the methods used in polymerisation are similar in all living organisms differing only in the type of polymer produced.

## Homopolymers, e.g. -A-A-A-A-A

Here an identical monomer is repeated along the chain. Polymerisation requires a single polymerase acting on the activated monomer ($A^*$) a reaction usually also requiring some polymer $[(A)_n]$ as a primer,

$$\text{i.e.} \quad (A)_n + A^* \rightarrow (A)_{n+1}$$

Consider two typical examples in microbiology.

(a) Polyglucoses

$(\text{glucose})_n + \text{ADPG} \rightarrow (\text{glucose})_{n+1} + \text{ADP}$

 where $(\text{glucose})_n$ = glycogen

 and ADPG = Adenosine diphosphate glucose

*or* $(\text{glucose})_n$ + glucose-fructose $\rightarrow (\text{glucose})_{n+1}$ + fructose

 where $(\text{glucose})_n$ = dextran, glucose-fructose = sucrose

(b) Poly-$\beta$-hydroxybutyrate

 $(\beta\text{-hydroxbutyrate})_n + \beta\text{-hydroxybutyryl CoA} \rightarrow (\beta\text{-hydroxybutyrate})_{n+1}$ + CoA

## Heteropolymers with a repeating unit (regular heteropolymers)

$$\text{e.g.} \quad \text{-A-B-C-A-B-C-A-B-C- or } (A\text{-}B\text{-}C)_n$$

Here more than one monomer occurs but the polymer is built up from repeating units of varying degrees of complexity. Polymerisation usually occurs by a preliminary biosynthesis of the activated repeated unit followed by its polymerisation

$$\text{i.e.} \quad A^* + B^* \rightarrow AB^*$$
$$AB^* + C^* \rightarrow ABC^*$$
$$(ABC)_n + ABC^* \rightarrow (ABC)_{n+1}$$

In this example, the specific nature of the polymer is determined by the specificity of three enzymes. Typical microbial polymers formed in this way are the heteropolysaccharides in the cell wall and capsule and the prokaryotic peptidoglycan.

## Heteropolymers without a repeating unit (irregular heteropolymers)

$$\text{e.g.} \quad \text{-A-D-A-C-B-D-A-A-}$$

The only examples of such heteropolymers in nature are the nucleic acids and proteins. In contrast to the previous examples where the nature of the polymer is determined by enzyme specificity, here it is determined by a coding or template mechanism and the general methods employed in transcription and in translation and the actual code used appear to be common to all living organisms. Their basis in the double-helix of DNA has almost passed into folk lore and will be assumed to be known to the reader of this book.

$$\text{i.e.} \quad \text{DNA} \longrightarrow \text{m-RNA} \longrightarrow \text{protein}$$
$$\downarrow$$
$$\text{DNA}$$

## CONVERSION OF CELL COMPONENTS TO A PHYSIOLOGICALLY ACTIVE STATE

Many of the chemical components of the cell are produced in a fully active state and at the site where they are required to fulfil their role. Thus soluble enzymes are formed in ribosomes and are released directly into the cytoplasm while many cell-wall macromolecules are polymerised at specific sites on the outside surface of the cytoplasmic membrane where the activated repeating units are joined to the cell wall *in situ* by the action of enzymes bound into the cytoplasmic membrane. On the other hand, other components require to be transported and incorporated into appropriate structures before they become fully active. Thus permease and electron-transport proteins are incorporated into cytoplasmic membrane, DNA and RNA polymerases into the nucleus, ribosomal proteins into ribosomes and so on. Presumably the proteins must have built-in recognition sites to ensure they finish up in the correct site in the cell although little is known of this very important process.

## THE NUTRITION OF MICROORGANISMS

We have seen that there are 100–200 monomers, coenzymes and other essential chemical components required for the growth of microorganisms. *These substances must either be synthesised by the cell itself or they must be supplied in the environment as nutrients.* In other words there is an inverse relationship between the biosynthetic capabilities of a microorganism and its nutritional requirements. Some cells are capable of synthesising all their cellular components from the basic metabolic building blocks and require only very simple growth media. Others can synthesise very few of their components and therefore have complex nutrient requirements. This range can be illustrated in the provision of organic nitrogenous compounds. The most important of these from the point of view of bulk requirements are the amino acids and nucleotides needed for protein and nucleic acid synthesis. Some microorganisms have the ability to utilise molecular nitrogen by a reduction process called *nitrogen fixation* leading to the production of ammonia which in turn is converted into organic nitrogen.

$$N_2 \xrightarrow[\text{nitrogen fixation}]{} NH_3 \xrightarrow{} \begin{array}{c}\text{Amino acids}\\\text{and nucleotides}\end{array}$$

Such nitrogen-fixing microorganisms are therefore capable of utilising atmospheric nitrogen as the sole nitrogen source; others require a fixed inorganic

70

form of nitrogen such as ammonia which can be converted into all the organic forms required; still others are incapable of the biosynthesis of most or all of their amino acids and nucleotides and thus require their nitrogen in a complex organic form.

Consider microorganisms with simple growth requirements. The main cellular elements are C, H, O, N, S and P. In a heterotroph carbon is provided by a suitable organic substance(s), H and O are provided by water whilst N, S and P can be given as inorganic ions such as ammonium, nitrate, sulphate or phosphate ions. Such organisms can be grown in a *synthetic or defined medium* in which typical components might be glucose, $NH_4Cl$, $Na_2SO_4$, $K_2HPO_4$, $MgSO_4$ and $FeSO_4$. The other essential elements for microbial growth (e.g. Mn, Ca, Co, Mo, Cu, Zn) are usually present in sufficient quantities as contaminants of the above components. For the growth of autotrophs, the carbon and energy source is left out and $CO_2$ is added. An appropriate electron donor may also be required and, in photoautotrophs, the cells must be illuminated.

A series of more complicated *synthetic media* can be made up to contain the additional nutrients required for a particular microorganism. For example, *Salmonella typhi* (the organism causing typhoid fever) requires the addition to a simple synthetic medium of only the amino acid tryptophane which it is unable to synthesise for itself. Other microorganisms have much more complex needs. Thus *Leuconostoc mesenteroides* requires in addition acetate, 19 amino acids, 4 purines and pyrimidines and 10 coenzymes (which, when required as nutrients, are usually called microbial vitamins); it obviously has a very restricted biosynthetic capability. These complex synthetic media are very expensive and tedious to make and their use is largely restricted to research purposes. In practice in the routine laboratory what is usually needed is a medium that will support the growth of as many microorganisms as possible, is reproducible in content and is cheap and easy to produce. A variety of such *general laboratory media* are manufactured, but most contain two main nutrient sources.

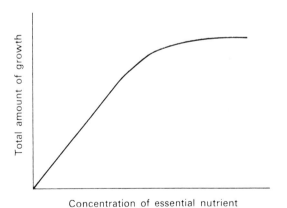

Concentration of essential nutrient

**Figure 5.4** Microbiological assay. The relationship between growth and the concentration of an essential nutrient

(1) A protein hydrolysate (sometimes called peptone) to provide C, energy, N and amino acids.

(2) A natural extract to provide other essential nutrients such as vitamins and inorganic salts. Meat or yeast extract are commonly employed but may, in addition, be supplemented by blood, serum or egg. An example of such a general laboratory medium is nutrient broth which usually contains 1–2% peptone, 1% meat extract and additional NaCl to bring the osmotic pressure up to the optimum for most bacteria.

## Microbiological assay

The realisation of the range of substances required for microbial growth and the specificity of these requirements led to the development of assay methods for these substances using microorganisms. If the total amount of microbial growth in batch culture is measured in a series of media containing variable amounts of a particular essential nutrient, results similar to those in Fig. 5.4 should be obtained. At lower levels of the essential nutrient there is a linear relationship between its concentration and the amount of growth (A to B). Above this region, the total amount of growth eventually becomes constant as some factor other than the level of the chosen essential nutrient limits growth. The linear part of the curve can then be used to assay the nutrient. In theory any substance required specifically for the growth of a microorganism can be assayed but the method has been particularly valuable for vitamins since they can be measured with a greater specificity and sensitivity than those of a chemical method.

## Nutritional evolution

It is usually assumed that those microorganisms with the simplest nutrient requirements are the most primitive on an evolutionary scale. In environments in which there is a plentiful supply of suitable nutrients, a far-ranging biosynthetic capacity would no longer be advantageous, indeed it might be disadvantageous since the cell would produce a lot of non-essential enzymes. If a microorganism inhabits such a rich environment as would a parasite, then it is assumed that a nutritional evolution would occur whereby a series of mutations cause the loss of biosynthetic pathways. The ultimate limits of nutritional evolution in a cellular organism would be reached in the chlamydia which do not even contain an energy-generating system and are dependant on the host cell for ATP as well as most other nutrients. In recompense for this host-dependence, the chlamydia have a much smaller enzymic repertoire and only contain about one-tenth as much DNA compared with a prokaryote having a full range of biosynthetic capacity.

There is a snag to this simple idea of nutritional evolution. The supposedly primitive organism with simple nutritional requirements is in fact the most sophisticated with respect to the number of enzymes it must produce. This enigma is discussed later (p. 90).

72

# 6 The reproduction of viruses

The system that has been generally used to study the reproduction of viruses is the attack of a bacterium by a bacteriophage or a phage as it is usually called. Indeed, much of the work has been confined to a series of phages attacking *Escherichia coli* called coliphages. They were chosen arbitrarily and called by the letter T and a number. In practice, three 'T-even' phages (T2, T4 and T6) having similar properties have been the ones chosen by most investigators. Although they have a rather complex structure for a virus (see p. 29), they have proved to be very suitable for experimental purposes and this Chapter will be largely concerned with results obtained with them, most of which can be applied to viruses in general.

## The counting of phages

It is difficult and unreliable to count viruses in the electron miscroscope and instead a viable count is carried out, the measure of viability being the ability

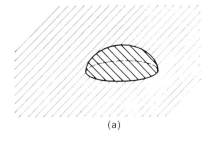

(a)

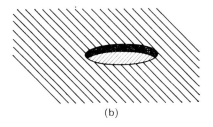

(b)

**Figure 6.1** A comparison of a bacterial colony with a phage plaque; (a) a bacterial colony growing on an agar plate, and (b) a phage plaque growing on a confluent bacterial lawn

73

of a phage to infect a sensitive bacterium, to multiply inside it and eventually to lyse it liberating fresh phages which attack neighbouring cells. In practice, a phage suspension is applied to a lawn of growing sensitive bacteria on an agar plate. A single phage will infect a cell, multiply, lyse it, and eventually cause a clear area or plaque on the plate where all the bacteria have been killed. This plaque is a virus colony (Fig. 6.1) and since it is produced from a single, viable organism, it can be used in the same way as cellular microorganisms for counting purposes.

### The one-step growth curve

The essential features of virus multiplication can be seen in the one-step growth curve experiment. A culture of sensitive bacteria is mixed with a relatively small number of phage particles and incubated for a short period to allow

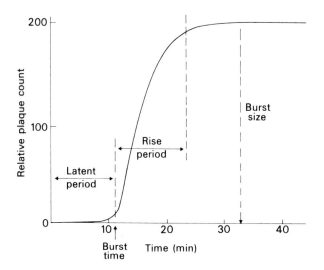

**Figure 6.2.** A one-step growth curve for a phage attacking a bacterium

adsorption of the phages onto the bacteria. The culture is diluted, allowed to grow and the number of phage particles plus infected bacteria is measured. It should be noted that a single plaque will be formed from either a phage particle or an infected bacterium irrespective of how many phages the latter may contain within it. Typical results are given in Fig. 6.2.

Initially there is a *latent period* in which there is no increase in the number of plaques. Suddenly there is a rapid rise in plaque-forming units as the bacteria begin to lyse liberating new phages. This *burst period* eventually levels out, the plaque count remaining more or less constant because the initial dilution of the culture largely prevents adsorption of newly liberated phages on the remaining uninfected bacteria. The factor by which the number of phage

74

particles increases in the experiment is known as the *burst size* and it represents the average number of phages produced on the lysis of one infected bacterial cell. The potential of virus multiplication is evident since the burst size is usually over a hundred and the whole process represented in the one-step growth curve may only take 10–20 minutes.

## THE MULTIPLICATION OF A PHAGE

The multiplication of a phage, as typified by the T-even coliphages, can be considered in three phases:
(1) Adsorption and penetration of the host.
(2) Production of new phage within the host.
(3) Lysis and liberation from the host.

### Adsorption and penetration of the host cell

If a suspension of virus particles is mixed with sensitive bacteria, the phages attach themselves to the cell surfaces of the host (Fig. 6.3a). This adsorption is a very specific process and can be likened to that between an enzyme and its substrate or to an antibody and the corresponding antigen. There are complementary sites in the phage tail fibres (see p. 29) and in the bacterial cell wall. The specific adsorption is followed by a further adsorption of the tail fibres onto

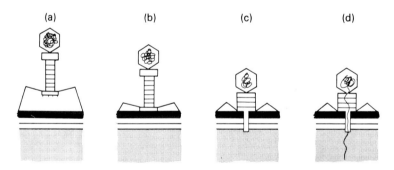

**Figure 6.3** The adsorption of a phage onto a sensitive host bacterium and the injection of the phage nucleic acid (for a description see the text)

the surface of the cell-wall (Fig. 6.3b). This is followed by a contraction of the tail sheath and the forcing of the tail core through the cell wall and cytoplasmic membrane (Fig. 6.3c). Finally the phage DNA enters the host cell (Fig. 6.3d) by a process analogous to injection by a hypodermic syringe although there is no actual contraction of the phage head; it is not known what causes the DNA to pass from the phage to the bacterium.

The end result of the above mechanism is that the protein capsid is left behind on the outside of the host cell while the nucleic acid passes in. This fascinating result was foreshadowed by the finding that if phage protein is specifically labelled with radioactive $^{35}S$ and phage DNA with radioactive $^{32}P$, then only the $^{32}P$ passes into the bacterial cytoplasm and plays any part in the production of further virus particles. It proved to be a key experiment in the development of molecular biology since it showed that only the phage nucleic acid was necessary to code for the production of complete mature phages. In other words, all the genetic information was in the phage DNA. Another striking illustration of the fact that the protein capsid is solely concerned in the passage of the infectious nucleic acid from one cell to another, is the observation that naked phage DNA itself can infect a cell if the permeability barriers of the bacterial wall are broken down such as in a protoplast; such infection leads to the production of normal phages.

## Production of new phages

The entry of the phage DNA into the host cell causes an almost immediate repression of the synthesis of host nucleic acid and protein. Instead, the metabolic machinery of the bacterium is turned over to the synthesis of polymers coded for by the phage DNA. Three phases can be distinguished.

(1) Under the influence of host RNA polymerase, a part only of the virus DNA is transcribed to m-RNA. This 'early' m-RNA is then translated by host ribosomes to produce 'early' proteins. These proteins are enzymes: although viral reproduction depends in the main upon host enzymes already present in the cell at the time of infection, additional virus-coded enzymes are essential or stimulatory to the later replication of phage DNA. For example, the T-even phages code for the synthesis of as many as 20 of such early enzymes. However, it must be emphasised that these proteins are not structural components and are not incorporated into the mature phage particle.

(2) The second phase consists of the synthesis of the structural protein and DNA of the phage. We have seen that the T-even phages have a relatively complex structure and that there will be many different protein subunits required. Such 'late' proteins are synthesised from 'late' m-RNA produced by regions of the phage genome not transcribed in the previous phase. At about the same time, new viral DNA is produced. We have thus produced all the components necessary to form the mature phage particle.

(3) The final stage is the assembly of these components. This assembly does not occur randomly with respect to time but instead occurs in a definite sequence or morphogenetic pattern. The viral DNA molecules condense under the influence of a 'late' protein called the condensing principle while the capsid subunits undergo self-assembly by a process analogous to crystallisation to form empty heads. The condensed DNA then passes into the empty heads. Similarly inevitable processes lead to phage tail and tail fibre assembly; all three then combine with the heads to give intact phage particles. Particular genes appear to be concerned in the proper sequencing of this assembly process.

76

The production of new phages can be summarised as follows:

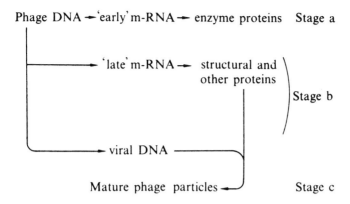

Phage DNA ─►'early' m-RNA ─► enzyme proteins    Stage a

'late' m-RNA ─► structural and
                other proteins

Stage b

viral DNA

Mature phage particles

Stage c

## Lysis and liberation from host

Associated with the assembly of mature phage particles, another late viral protein with a lysozyme-like activity similar to that in the phage tail, is produced in the host cytoplasm. This enzyme catalyses the partial hydrolysis of the bacterial peptidoglycan causing a weakening of the cell wall and an eventual osmotic rupture. The phages are thus liberated into the environment where they go on to infect other cells and to start the whole process again.

Although this description of the phases of virus multiplication is for the more complex DNA phages, in general it applies to all viruses. However, RNA-viruses require a special mechanism for the self-replication of the RNA by transcription; in this way the RNA behaves as though it were DNA by reproducing itself as well as acting as a m-RNA. There are also variations in the way in which the viral nucleic acid enters the cell. For example, in the simple plant viruses there is no specific adsorption or entry mechanism but passage occurs through breaks or cuts in the plant surface and is frequently insect-mediated. Animal viruses are carried into the cell by phagocytic or pinocytic action and it is only then that the nucleic acid becomes separated from the capsid; release often occurs without lysis by a process analogous to a reversed pinocytosis.

Whatever the refinements of virus multiplication, the process is clearly different from that occurring in cellular life where the cell maintains its integrity even in an intracellular parasite. In other words, viruses always carry out a sort of genetic parasitism by taking over the nucleic acid and protein-synthesising machinery of the host. This property, together with their quite different structure, their lack of metabolic machinery and the absence of a form intermediate between them and cells, leads to the view that viruses have been derived by an evolutionary development of intracellular nucleic acid-containing structures into self-reproducing entities rather than by a gradual specialisation of a cell to a more parasitic existence. For example, we can imagine a chromosome, part of a chromosome or a ribosome becoming free from normal cellular control mechanisms. Such a view is strengthened by the fact that under certain circumstances viruses can actually become incorporated into the cell and reproduce synchronously with it. In bacteriophages, this process is known as lysogeny.

## LYSOGENY

In *virulent* phages, the entry of the viral nucleic acid leads to an irreversible series of events culminating in cell lysis and the liberation of the progeny. However, an alternative mechanism exists in many viruses by which the DNA, after entry into the host cytoplasm, becomes integrated into the host genome and reproduces in phase with it in a form known as a *prophage* (see Fig. 6.4). This

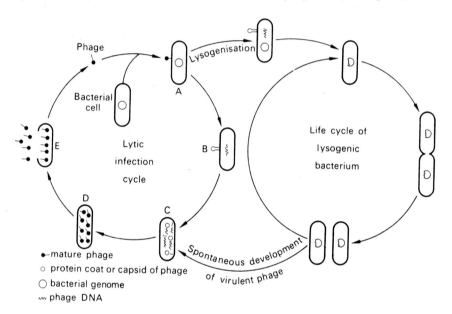

**Figure 6.4**   The cycles of lytic infection by a virulent phage and lysogeny by a temperate phage

virus—bacterium relationship is called lysogeny and those phages that can be integrated are called *temperate* to distinguish them from the virulent ones discussed above. We know the prophage continues to be reproduced in synchrony with the lysogenised bacterium for two reasons.

(1) Occasionally there is a spontaneous initiation of a lytic cycle of development, the rate of which can be increased by certain inducing agents.

(2) The phenotypic properties of a bacterium are often changed by the presence of prophage. In particular, the lysogenised bacteria become immune to further attack by related phages. However, more specific alterations may occur and these become important when it is realised that a large proportion of bacteria in nature are in fact lysogenised. For example, the chemical structure of the surface antigens may be affected by the presence of prophage and in the

78

bacterium causing the disease of diphtheria, the virulence and toxicity of the organism is related to lysogeny. An interesting question is how far such stable associations of viruses and cells can occur with other hosts. For example, there is evidence that viruses can cause cancer by being incorporated into an animal cell and transforming it thereby into a cancerous cell. How far viruses are responsible for cancer in general, we don't know.

## MICROORGANISMS AND VIRUSES

The majority of prokaryotes can be attacked by a suitable virus. Some bacteriophages have the complex structure of the T-even coliphages, others have a simpler naked icosahedron shape, while a few are filamentous. Viruses also attack blue-green algae and show similar characteristics to bacteriophages. The position regarding viral infection of eukaryotic microorganisms is less clear and the only well-established instances are some viruses attacking fungi. For example, such viruses may cause problems in the mushroom industry. The reasons for the resistance of algae, most fungi and protozoa to virus infection are not known and the phenomenon may be more apparent than real due to a lack of proper investigation. However, there can be little doubt that viruses do not commonly attack yeasts since such infections would almost certainly have been observed as a result of the widespread use of yeast in industry.

# 7 The genetics of microorganisms

There has been a remarkable turnabout in our understanding of the genetics of microorganisms, and particularly of bacteria, in the last quarter of a century. The school of pleomorphism, which believed in a single infinitely variable microbe, was overthrown as a result of the isolation of pure cultures but this led to the other extreme—a feeling that microorganisms were invariable. This view was held in spite of its contrariness to the general variability of life and although there were many observations against it. Many even doubted whether bacteria possessed a nucleus, chromosomes or genes. One reason for this state of affairs was that the small size of the microorganisms made it usually necessary to deal with large populations of cells. Yet nowadays microbes have become the organisms of choice in much work on fundamental problems in genetics, and they have been invaluable in the development of our understanding of heredity at a molecular level. The key observation that genes act by controlling the specificity of protein synthesis was initiated by work with the fungus *Neurospora crassa* and led to the formulation of general theory in the equation

$$1 \text{ gene} = 1 \text{ enzyme}$$

Bacteria and, in particular, *Escherichia coli* have been used to define this relationship in more depth

$$\text{i.e.} \quad 1 \text{ DNA gene (or cistron)} = 1 \text{ polypeptide}$$

We have said that this process occurs through the intermediary formation of a molecule or m-RNA by means of a code which appears to be universal to all living organisms.

The majority of genes, then, produce a specific polypeptide which may act directly or in combination with other polypeptides to form enzymes or structural proteins. Such genes are called *structural genes*. We have also mentioned that bacteria are capable of controlling the synthesis of specific proteins by such processes as induction and repression (see pp. 67–8). A study of these processes has led to the view that structural genes controlling the synthesis of physiologically-related proteins usually occur as a cluster on a chromosome, the region being called an *operon*. Such multigenic operons produce single molecules of m-RNA, a transcription process organised by an *operator gene* at one end of the operon and initiated by the binding of an RNA polymerase to a *promoter gene* situated next to the operator gene. It is the operator genes which are controlled by the action of polypeptides produced by other so-called *regulator genes* (see Fig. 7.1). The basic action of these regulatory polypeptides is usually to combine with the operator genes, thus preventing the binding of

80

RNA polymerase to the promoter gene and thereby inhibiting m-RNA synthesis and so the synthesis of the proteins coded for by the operon. In other words, control is essentially negative although some examples of positive control have also been found. Consider the processes of induction and repression discussed in more detail.

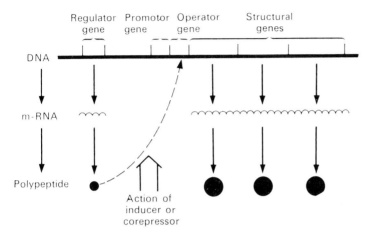

**Figure 7.1**   The different types of genes and their control in prokaryotes. The inducer or corepressor acts on the product of the regulator gene by the mechanism discussed on pp. 67 and 68

## Induction

The polypeptide produced by the regulator gene represses the operator gene. However, the inducer specifically combines with this polypeptide repressor rendering it incapable of acting on the operator gene and thereby switching on induced protein synthesis.

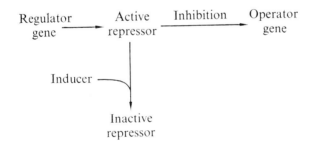

## End-product repression

The polypeptide or aporepressor produced by the regulator gene has no effect on the operator gene until it specifically combines with the end-product or corepressor when it becomes capable of reacting with the operator gene and so switches off protein synthesis.

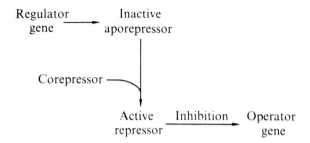

There are two examples of the way in which protein synthesis can be controlled and they provide a model for the type of system that may operate in higher cells and organisms. However, the speed of response to environmental stimuli depends upon the stability of m-RNA molecules. In bacteria such molecules have an average lifetime as short as 2–3 minutes and this allows rapid shifts in the direction of protein synthesis. Similar mechanisms may be concerned in switching on and off specific protein synthesis in sporulation and germination (p. 20) and for more sophisticated examples of differentiation. Studies like these on the molecular basis of genetics are now well known, but they have only been possible by the availability of suitable mutants and of methods for recombination in prokaryotes. Most of this chapter must be concerned with mutagenesis and recombination.

## MUTATION IN MICROORGANISMS

A wide variety of heritable changes in the properties of bacteria have been shown to be due to the selection of mutants. Some typical examples are as follows:

(1) *Auxotrophic mutants.* We have seen that many microorganisms such as *Escherichia coli* can grow on a medium containing a single carbon and energy source. They are called *prototrophs*. If a mutation occurs resulting in the loss of the ability to synthesise an essential metabolite such as an amino acid or a growth factor, it will express itself in a nutritional requirement for the substance. Such mutants are called *auxotrophs* and they have been used as markers for genetic experiments, as a means of elucidating the relationship between genes and enzymes and for discovering metabolic pathways.

(2) *Resistant mutants.* Resistance to antimicrobial agents and to phage can occur by the selection of appropriate mutants. Acquired resistance of this type can have serious consequences since it means that a particular antimicrobial agent can no longer be used in the treatment of an infection.

(3) *Mutation leading to changes in cell surface polymers.* Changes in the nature of the surface layers can often be recognised easily since they can also result in changes in colony form on solid media. For example, the pneumococcus as isolated from a patient with pneumonia produces a sticky mucoid colony due to the biosynthesis of a hygroscopic capsular polysaccharide. Subculture in the laboratory commonly results in the selection of non-mucoid colonial mutants which no longer produce capsular polysaccharides nor cause the disease of pneumonia. In other words they are avirulent. This is the result of a mutational loss of an enzyme specifically concerned in extracellular polysaccharide biosynthesis.

These are but some of the mutations commonly encountered in nature and in the laboratory. Of course most genes are mutable at comparable rates, but it may not be easy to recognise or to isolate the mutant. However, an important question which in the past has had philosophical and even political implications is whether these mutations occur spontaneously or are directed? For example, take mutation to penicillin resistance, unfortunately a not uncommon occurrence in medicine. Does penicillin direct this mutation or does it simply select out a naturally-occurring spontaneous mutant? Mathematical analysis of the occurrence of mutants has shown the process is indeed a spontaneous one and special methods have even allowed the isolation of penicillin-resistant mutants without ever exposing the cells to penicillin. However, although mutations in microorganisms are spontaneous and undirected, mutagens such as ultraviolet light, ionising radiations and chemical substances such as nitrous acid and nucleotide analogues can be used to produce a *generalised* increase in the mutation rate.

Viruses are also mutable although only when they are growing in the host cell; the nucleic acid in the intact virus is protected from the action of most mutagens.

## Mutations and microbial adaptability

The process of Darwinian evolution, that is the selection of spontaneous mutants by the environment and the exchange of genes by recombination, can occur very rapidly in the microorganisms. Although mutation rates are similar to those in higher organisms, various factors will lead to a faster rate of evolution.

(1) All prokaryotes and many eukaryotic microorganisms are normally haploid so a mutation cannot be masked by an allelic gene.

(2) They are unicellular, so any mutated cell can give rise to a new evolutionary line.

(3) Microorganisms can occur at high population densities in restricted environments giving a good chance of a mutant being present in a particular ecological niche where it may have an advantage.

(4) Microorganisms grow very rapidly and can be subject to high selective pressures. Thus if we inoculate a nutrient medium containing penicillin with a penicillin-sensitive bacterium, the wild-type organisms will be unable to grow. However, any penicillin-resistant mutants will multiply and after incubation

overnight should be the dominant population. In other words, evolution with respect to the character of penicillin-resistance has occurred overnight.

As a result of this capability of rapid evolutionary adaptation, microorganisms and, in particular, prokaryotes have been able to adapt themselves to a wide variety of extreme environments (see Chapter 5). Another consequence which can cause considerable embarrassment is that they can change rapidly during laboratory subculture. The environment of a normal growth medium is often wildly different from that normally encountered in nature and a few subcultures may be sufficient to select a series of mutants adapted to growth in this new environment. We have already seen an example in the pneumococcus which loses its ability to cause pneumonia and to produce a capsule (p. 83). Presumably the non-capsulate form has a growth advantage under laboratory conditions whereas the capsulate form is selected in the animal host since it is not subject to phagocytosis (p. 22). It must be realised that a single bacterial colony may contain as many as $10^8$ cells. A bacterium will have at least $10^3$ genes and each will have a mutation frequency of about $1 \times 10^{-8}$. So a single colony may contain about a thousand mutants. In other words, a pure culture is a figment of the imagination, a very worrying thought to the microbiologist. A given environment will eventually select out those mutants which happen to grow faster or die slower in it and once this happens, the culture should remain stable. Although many of the changes that occur in these processes may be minor and do not result in any obvious changes in the properties of the microorganism under study, they may be important if we desire to apply laboratory experimental results to events occurring in a natural environment. What can be done to prevent such a selection occurring in the laboratory? All we can do is to choose environmental conditions to mimic as far as possible those occurring in nature and hope thereby to minimise change. An alternative is to avoid subculture by preserving the cells in a state of suspended animation by freeze-drying or, better still, by keeping them at liquid nitrogen temperatures. However, not all microorganisms will survive such treatments.

# GENETIC RECOMBINATION IN MICROORGANISMS

## Recombination in prokaryotes

We have seen that genetic changes occurring as a result of mutation can result in the acquisition of new biological characteristics and thereby allow evolutionary change. However, evolution of the fittest organism in a particular environment will be aided if transfer of genes between one organism and another is made possible by genetic recombination. Compared with the ordered nature of sexual recombination in eukaryotes, the process in prokaryotes is less well developed, occurs rather spasmodically and does not involve a true fusion of a male and female gamete to produce a diploid zygote. Instead there is transference of only some genes from the donor cell to produce a partial diploid. This is illustrated in Fig. 7.2.

There are three mechanisms by which these DNA fragments can pass from

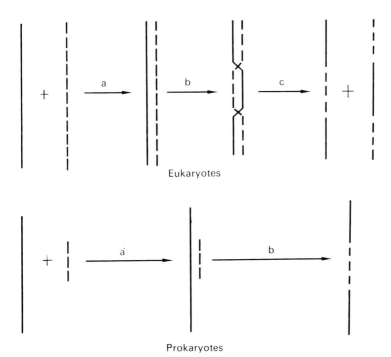

Eukaryotes

Prokaryotes

**Figure 7.2** A simplified representation of genetic recombination in eukaryotes and prokaryotes. In the former two haploid chromosomes, one from each parent, come together in the diploid nucleus (a); at some stage prior to meiosis these undergo crossing over (b, c) to give haploid cells with redistributed genes. In prokaryotes, a DNA fragment combines with the corresponding region in the recipient cell (a) and crossing over results in the elimination of the fragment of DNA produced as a result (b)

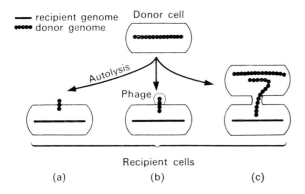

**Figure 7.3** Recombination methods in prokaryotes. a, transformation; b, transduction; c, conjugation

a donor to a recipient cell—transformation, transduction and conjugation (Fig. 7.3).

(1) *Transformation.* This process was discovered in one of the key experiments of molecular biology. We have seen that virulence in pneumococci is determined by the ability to produce an extracellular capsular polysaccharide (p. 83). Indeed pneumococci can be divided into about a hundred types which differ in the chemical nature of the capsular polysaccharides and hence in the specificity of the enzymes involved in their biosynthesis. It was found that it was possible to transform one type of pneumococcus to another by adding an extract of the second type

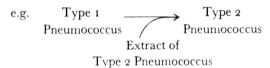

The substance in the extract responsible for transformation was purified and shown to be DNA. In the example given, the DNA of Type 2 cells had entered the Type 1 cells and the genes concerned in capsular polysaccharide biosynthesis had undergone recombination resulting in the insertion of Type 2 genes in place of the corresponding Type 1 genes. The historical importance of the finding would be difficult to exaggerate since it showed clearly that DNA was the unit of heredity—in other words that genes are made of DNA. This was confirmed by the finding that other pneumococcal genes could be transferred in a similar way. However, the process seems to be restricted to a few bacterial genera and the key factors probably lie in the ability of a large molecule like DNA to enter the cell and reach the nucleus. In transformable cells an important property appears to be a binding of the DNA to the cell surface prior to uptake.

The process of transformation is probably unique to prokaryotes and fortunately visions of the controlled genetic engineering of humans by adding appropriate DNA molecules are little more than a remote possibility at the moment.

(2) *Transduction.* This process is similar to transformation except that the DNA fragment passing from the donor to the recipient is incorporated into a phage. The donor cell is attacked by a phage, and in the process of virus maturation, some bacterial genes are incorporated. The incomplete viral DNA, on entering the recipient cell, is normally unable to initiate the process of multiplication or lysogeny, but instead the incorporated bacterial genes undergo recombination with the recipient DNA.

(3) *Conjugation.* In this process cell contact is necessary. Transfer of DNA from the donor or 'male' cell to the recipient or 'female' cell involves special pili (p. 20) called 'sex pili' or F-pili, which form a bridge between the cells. The DNA passes through the channel in the centre of the pilus resulting in an orderly entry of genes according to their arrangement on the chromosome. Although in theory the whole chromosome can be transferred, the process is

probably rarely complete in practice. An additional complication occurs in conjugation. Whilst in both transformation and transduction any cell can in theory act as a donor or a recipient, in conjugation some cells are female and some are male in the sense that some are donors of DNA while others are recipients. What determines this primitive form of sex? Two experiments throw light on the problem.

(a) A female can be changed to a male by contact with a male, a process involving a passage of an infectious agent present in the male called a 'sex factor' or 'F-agent' apparently made of DNA.

$$\text{Female (F}-) \xrightarrow[\text{Male (F}+)]{} \text{Male (F}+)$$

It is assumed that these F-agents exist in the cytoplasm of the male rather like phage genomes and the sad conclusion can be reached that 'maleness' in bacteria resembles a chronic virus infection.

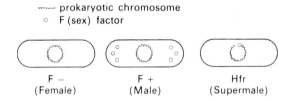

prokaryotic chromosome
○  F (sex) factor

F –          F +          Hfr
(Female)     (Male)       (Supermale)

**Figure 7.4**   The different sexual stages of prokaryotic cells

(b) A male (F + ) can mutate to a 'supermale' which shows a much higher frequency of recombination with a female (hence the mutant is called Hfr). In such Hfr strains, the F-agent is incorporated into the main chromosome where it duplicates in phase with nuclear division.

These states are summarised in Fig. 7.4.

## Episomes and plasmids

Bacteriophages and F-factors normally have the common ability of being based on DNA molecules capable of existing in two forms.

(1) An autonomously reproducing state as in a bacterium infected with a virulent phage or in F + cells.

(2) An integrated state in which they are incorporated into the main bacterial genome as in the prophage of lysogenic bacteria (p. 78) or in Hfr cells.

Such DNA elements existing in two forms are called *episomes*. In addition there is another class of extra-nuclear DNA elements which are only capable of existing in an autonomously-reproducing state, dividing in phase with cell division and behaving like secondary and dispensable chromosomes. They are called *plasmids* and they contain genes which are inessential for normal existence such as those controlling resistance to antimicrobial agents. Such 'resistance' plasmids pose an even greater threat to chemotherapy than spontaneous mutations since their transfer to a previously-sensitive bacterium may result in the simultaneous acquirement of resistance to many antibiotics in current use.

*The importance of recombination in prokaryotes*

Are these recombination methods important in nature or are they largely laboratory artefacts? It is difficult to be categorical. Certainly transformation and conjugation seem to have a restricted occurrence in prokaryotes. On the other hand, transduction appears to be much more common; most bacteria can be attacked by phages, many of which are capable of transduction. Furthermore, it must be realised that relatively rare processes may be of considerable importance in the evolution of new strains. What, then, has been the value of these methods in the laboratory? Here there is no doubt that they have proved invaluable in the development of molecular genetics; they have allowed genetic mapping not only of genes within a chromosome but also the fine structure of genes and the relationship of this fine structure to the DNA molecule itself.

## Recombination in eukaryotes

Genetic recombination in eukaryotes is essentially a sexual process involving recombination during the process of meiosis leading to the eventual production

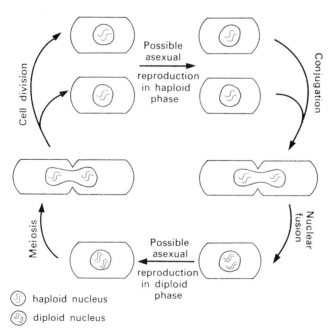

**Figure 7.5**  The alternation of generations in a eukaryote

88

of male and female haploid gametes. Fusion of such gametes results in the formation of new types of diploids. The alternation of a haploid and a diploid generation (Fig. 7.5) is characteristic of most eukaryotic microorganisms although there is a wide variation both in the relative importance of the haploid and diploid phases for vegetative reproduction and in the degree of sexual differentiation they exhibit. Thus in fungi the predominant phase may be haploid or diploid or there may be a roughly equal role of both: morphologically-distinct male and female forms can exist or there may be sexual conjugation between two similar cells derived from the same clone.

One important characteristic of eukaryotic genetics is the presence of extra-nuclear genetic DNA in organelles such as mitochondria and chloroplasts (see p. 22), and these are in some ways analogous to the autonomously-reproducing plasmids and episomes of prokaryotes.

## THE ORIGIN OF LIFE AND THE EVOLUTION OF MICROORGANISMS

It is tempting to believe that the variety of life on earth was all derived from a single primitive organism which had developed the powers of self-reproduction and evolutionary development. This is strikingly confirmed by the basic similarity in the biochemistry and genetics of living organisms as we know them. They all contain the same amino acids and nucleotides polymerised using basically the same mechanism and code. If, then, we assume that all living organisms have been derived from a primitive 'microorganism', what can be said about the nature of this organism, its formation and its later development? Much must be surmised, but there are few facts to go on.

(1) The earth is about $4.5 \times 10^9$ years old; in the early stages the main elements which make up living organisms were in a reduced form. Thus carbon, oxygen and nitrogen were predominantly present as methane, water and ammonia while the main component of the atmosphere was hydrogen.

(2) Experiments in which such a reducing environment is reproduced as far as possible in the laboratory, have shown that under the conditions existing on the earth about $3 \times 10^9$ years ago, a variety of sugar, amino acids, purines, pyrimidines and fatty acids would be formed by purely chemical means. The energy for these syntheses would be provided mainly by ultraviolet rays from the sun which in those days would have been more intense due to the lack of an absorbing layer of ozone in the upper atmosphere

$$\text{i.e.} \quad NH_3, CH_4, H_2O \xrightarrow[\text{UV light}]{} \text{organic compounds}$$

Further experiments have shown that some of these molecules might be expected to polymerise to form macromolecules. This process of *chemical evolution* would have caused a gradual accumulation of organic compounds to form a 'primordial soup' since there would be no microorganisms to break them down.

(3) Not long ago the idea that fossil microorganisms might occur would have

89

been considered fanciful. Now the examination of thin sections of rocks have provided reasonably good evidence for microbial fossils about $3 \times 10^9$ years old —in other words at about the time conditions might have been suitable for life to evolve in terms of the chemical evolution described previously. These first organisms appear to be primitive prokaryotes. Eukaryotes, recognisable by their characteristically shaped inorganic walls (e.g. diatoms and foraminifera), appeared about $1 \times 10^9$ years ago.

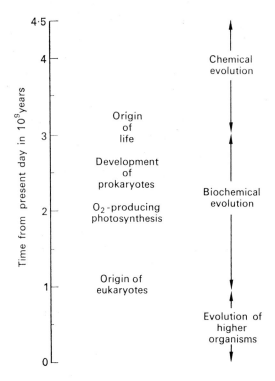

**Figure 7.6** A possible course of biological evolution on earth

(4) About $2 \times 10^9$ years ago the atmosphere began to change from a reduced to an oxidised state. Oxygen and nitrogen gradually became the predominant gases. This change was almost certainly due to the development of oxygen-producing photosynthetic organisms—probably prokaryotes like the blue-green algae. This time-scale is summarised in Fig. 7.6.

### The origin and development of prokaryotes

It is difficult to visualise the process of the development of our 'primitive prokaryote' from the primordial soup although we must realise that plenty of time was available for the process. Certainly a first stage must have been the development of a semipermeable membrane to allow the concentration and retention of essential molecules. In fact one of the properties of the polymers found in laboratory 'primordial soup' experiments is the tendency to form colloidal microspheres of bacterial dimensions with some semipermeable properties. From such aggregates might have been developed simple metabolic systems and a machinery for multiplication and heredity. We know nothing about this early stage of biochemical evolution although there has been much speculation on its possible inevitability and thus of the inevitable occurrence on other planets of organisms with a biochemistry similar to ours. However, we can make some reasonable guesses on the later developments on this planet of these primitive prokaryotes. The following stages may have occurred:

*Stage 1* The evolution of an anaerobic heterotroph obtaining its energy by substrate-level phosphorylation and its complex nutrient requirements from the primordial soup.

*Stage 2* As the level of organic nutrients in the environment was reduced by their microbial utilisation, new biosynthetic pathways would be evolved resulting in simpler nutrient requirement.

*Stage 3* The development of an electron-transport system would allow the more efficient oxidative phosphorylation to occur. However, in the probable absence of oxygen, anaerobic respiration only would be possible.

*Stage 4* The electron-transport system developed in Stage 3 could evolve into one for photosynthetic phosphorylation since we have seen that the processes are very similar. Eventually an oxygen-producing photosynthesis would develop.

*Stage 5* As oxygen began to accumulate in the atmosphere, aerobic heterotrophs could develop.

In this way, the major biochemical groupings of prokaryotes would be formed and could develop into the types we know today.

## The evolution of eukaryotes

We have said that there are indications that mitochondria have been developed from parasitic aerobic prokaryotes and chloroplasts from parasitic oxygen-producing photosynthetic prokaryotes such as blue-green algae (see p. 23). If this is so, the ancestor of the primitive eukaryote must have been a large microorganism obtaining its energy by glycolytic substrate-level phosphorylation. Association with intracellular prokaryotes having more efficient energy-producing systems would obviously have been advantageous and this symbiotic relationship could eventually have become obligatory resulting in the transfer of some of the functions of the intracellular prokaryotic nucleus to the host cell nucleus. Gradually the eukaryote as we know it would develop and with it a much greater capacity for the evolutionary development of multicellularity would occur. So higher organisms would evolve although at the same time microorganisms would have advantages in many ecological situations and would also continue to evolve.

# 8 Associations between micro-organisms and higher organisms

Microorganisms have many effects on man, some direct, some indirect, some beneficial and some harmful. As a result of Koch's demonstration in the last century of the ability of specific microbes to cause specific diseases to man, microbiology has been dominated by their harmful effects and it is only recently that more attention has been paid to their positive value. This and the next chapter will give some illustration of the many ways they can affect us.

It is common in nature for microorganisms to be associated in some way with a host. Microorganisms can form such relationships with other microorganisms, with animals or with plants and as a result may gain protection, a useful source of nutrients or other benefits. The host may be unaffected in which case the relationship is called *commensalism*, it may gain (i.e. *symbiosis*) or it may lose (i.e. *parasitism*). However, the following points should be noted concerning such relationships.

(1) It can be argued that in a close relationship of the type implied, the host cannot be unaffected and hence the term commensalism has little meaning other than in a relative sense.

(2) The borderline between symbiosis and parasitism may not always be clear. Indeed some biologists use the term 'symbiosis' in its original meaning of 'living together' and then divide symbiotic relationships into mutualistic symbiosis (i.e. symbiosis) and parasitic symbiosis (i.e. parasitism). Symbiosis can also be divided into endosymbiosis in which one organism lives within the cells or tissues of the host and ectosymbiosis in which the symbionts live separately. However, there is a danger that such tidy-mindedness will lead to a rigid compartmentation which gives a false idea of ecological relationships in nature. In this book, the terms symbiosis and parasitism will be used in their more common sense.

(3) It must be emphasised that the advantage gained to the microorganism by an association with a host must be considered in terms of the population rather than the individual.

## SYMBIOSIS

In order to illustrate the gradation from an apparently commensal relationship to a symbiotic one, let us consider two systems—the mammalian gut and the plant root.

### Microorganisms and the mammalian gut

The majority of microorganisms in the gut occur in the small and large intes-

92

tines, the acidity of the stomach being sufficient to prevent the growth and to cause the death of most microorganisms. A few acid-tolerant bacteria can colonise the lining of the stomach but their effect on the host is unknown. As we pass from the small to the large intestine and to the bowels, the concentration of microorganisms increases so that they make up about a third of the weight of faeces. In some ways, therefore, the gut resembles a continuous culture system with an entry port in the mouth and an exit port at the anus.

What are these intestinal microorganisms and what is their effect? Surprisingly enough the majority of them have only been grown in the laboratory in recent years and it used to be thought that most were facultative anaerobes like *E. coli*. Indeed, before its contemporary claim to fame, the main importance of *E. coli* to the microbiologist was as a measure of the faecal contamination of drinking water, the number of the organisms in a unit volume giving a reasonable indication of the contamination. However, it now seems that most gut organisms are very strict anaerobes which are killed by even the small amounts of oxygen normally used in laboratory subculture and special methods are necessary for their isolation. In the intestines these strict anaerobes are reliant on the facultative anaerobes to remove oxygen from the environment. Although we now know the nature of most of the normal gut flora, their effect on the animal host is less clear. It used to be thought that the microorganisms were essentially commensals but more recent evidence renders this unlikely. It is possible to produce animals growing in the complete absence of microorganisms against infection, and such 'germ-free' creatures have poorly-developed defence mechanisms, have an abnormal gut and have increased nutritional needs compared with normal animals. Some of these effects can also be produced in humans undergoing medical treatment using wide-spectrum antibiotics; the majority of the gut flora are killed and as a result the normally harmless microorganisms remaining may become dangerous. Evidently our gut bacteria perform a useful but not an irreplaceable function and we should avoid their removal.

A more obvious example of symbiosis is in the gut of ruminants, those herbivorous animals such as cattle, sheep and goats which use plant cellulose as the

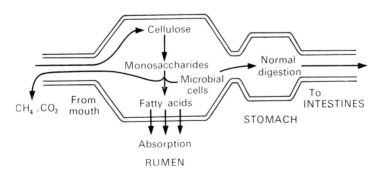

**Figure 8.1.** A diagrammatic representation of the metabolism occurring in the rumen

major source of their diet. Cellulose cannot be digested in a normal gut, but the ruminants have developed a special region for the purpose—the rumen which is essentially a large fermentation vat (about 100 litres in the cow) into which masticated plant materials enter to be digested by the large numbers of anaerobic bacteria and protozoa there. These symbiotic microorganisms hydrolyse cellulose and other plant polysaccharides to their component monosaccharides which are then fermented to simple fatty acids and to methane and carbon dioxide. The fatty acids are absorbed from the rumen and are used by the animals as a carbon and energy source while the microbial cells produced pass into the stomach where they are digested in the normal way to provide the other nutrients (e.g. vitamins and much of the protein) required for growth. The process is summarised in Fig. 8.1. The similarity of the rumen to a continuous culture fermentation is striking and recently chemostats have been built in the laboratory to simulate its action.

### Microorganisms and the plant root

In general, healthy plant leaves and stems do not provide a suitable environment for a large amount of microbial growth. On the other hand, the roots are surrounded by a region called the rhizosphere where microbial nutrients are provided by excretion from the plant and where the environmental conditions do not fluctuate so much as above ground. Consequently the level of microorganisms may be many times greater than in the soil away from root influence. The action of such rhizosphere organisms is not entirely clear but they appear to be normally commensals. However, a more organised relationship can exist with fungi in which the hyphae form an external sheath around the root and may even penetrate it. These mycorrhizae, as they are called, confer an advantage to plants growing in poor soils where where they aid in the

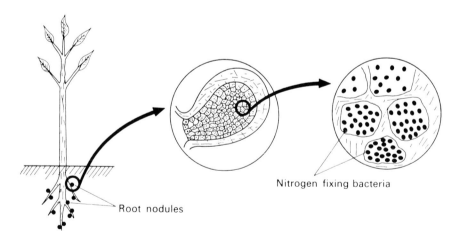

Nitrogen fixing bacteria

Root nodules

**Figure 8.2**   Symbiotic nitrogen fixation showing a plant with root nodules and two magnifications of cross section through a nodule

94

absorption of essential nutrients by increasing the area for absorption. The growth of forest trees is particularly improved by such a relationship.

A most striking example of a well-developed symbiotic relationship is between bacteria of the genus *Rhizobium* and leguminous plants (beans, clover, peas, etc.). The rhizobia infect the plant via the root hairs and invade the tissues. Some of the plant cells are infected intracellularly and as a result enlarge, divide and eventually produce characteristic nodules each of which may contain as many as $10^9$ bacteria (Fig. 8.2). The importance of the relationship lies in the combined ability of the plant and the rhizobia to fix atmospheric nitrogen (see p. 70). Such symbiotic-nitrogen fixation is an exceedingly important process in agriculture since the limiting factor for plant growth is often the level of a suitable combined nitrogen source. A crop of leguminous plants such as clover may fix as much as 350 kg of nitrogen per hectare (about 400 lb/acre) in a season compared with only about 5 kg/hectare for free-living nitrogen-fixing bacteria in temperate regions of the world or up to 60 kg/hectare by blue-green algae in the tropics. The importance of nitrogen fixation to the nitrogen cycle as a whole is discussed in the next chapter.

### Symbiosis between microorganisms

The best-known examples of symbiosis between microorganisms are the *lichens* in which fungi live in association with algae. Lichens are common in situations in which other forms of life are unable to survive such as exposed rock surfaces and tree trunks. The association is one in which both partners become modified to give complex structures in which the bulk is made up from fungal hyphae that surround and penetrate a layer of algae (Fig. 8.3). Both symbionts can be grown separately and have been brought together to form a lichen if the environmental conditions became unfavourable to their separate growth. The deleterious conditions required for this symbiosis in the laboratory correspond to the type of ecological situations in which lichens are found; that is, scarcity of

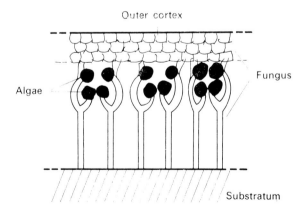

**Figure 8.3** The structure of a lichen seen in section

nutrients and extremes of wetting and, in particular, of drying. The symbiotic relationship in lichens is one in which the alga supplies the fungus with organic nutrients produced by photosynthesis while the fungus supplies the alga with a protective environment. The lichen itself has a marked ability to scavenge and to concentrate the limited nutrients available, an ability that makes them sensitive indicators of air pollution. Most species are rapidly killed as the concentration of toxic pollutants rises and therefore cannot grow in industrial areas.

## PARASITISM

In any parasitic relationship between a microorganism and a higher organism, a cycle occurs. The parasite enters the host usually at some specific entry point; this entry is followed by consolidation and multiplication within the host and finally by dissemination, usually again at some specific exit point, to allow infection of other hosts. In considering the factors in this relationship, we will be taking examples mainly from animal infections since more is known about them and the means of defence against them. This selection must in no sense minimise the importance of the many other parasitic relationships that can occur and which have great impact both economically and ecologically.

(1) *Entry into the host.* Animals and plants have adapted their outer surfaces to provide a barrier to invasion which is normally broken only by damage or by means of a special entry mechanism such as by an insect bite. However, there are particular areas on the host that are less protected and can more readily allow entry. Microorganisms parasitic on animals are usually specialised to one of these areas such as the gut, the respiratory tract or the urinogenital system and those on plants to stomata or lenticils.

(2) *Multiplication.* Once the microorganism reaches a suitable region of the host and provided it has not been killed by the host defence mechanisms, multiplication occurs. The *pathogenicity* of an organism represents the ability of a parasite to gain entry and multiply eventually causing the physiological and anatomical changes characteristic of a disease. This pathogenicity is usually very specific in terms of the host attacked. Thus most diseases affecting domestic animals are fortunately not transmitted to man and vice versa. The few that are transmitted may cause a much milder form of the disease, a fact made use of in vaccination against smallpox by using a related virus attacking cows (cowpox). The degree of pathogenicity is termed the *virulence* of a microorganism. A highly virulent strain may require only a single cell to cause an infection whereas others may need the entry of a large number of cells. Whilst pathogenicity is often used to define a species, variations in virulence commonly occur within the strains of a species. It is also possible to obtain mutants varying in their virulence (e.g. p. 83) and such mutants are useful in defining the physical basis of virulence by comparison with the properties of the wild type. They are also valuable since avirulent mutants can induce a resistance to
96

the disease without causing the dangerous symptoms and in this way they can be used as live vaccines.

The multiplication of a pathogen is usually confined to certain specific areas of the host. Thus the organism causing the disease of brucellosis in cattle grows preferentially in the foetus and the placenta of a pregnant cow, usually resulting in abortion. The reason for this localisation within the host is that the growth of these bacteria is markedly stimulated by the presence of erythritol, a sugar absent from the tissues of the cow except for those specifically associated with the foetus. However, in most cases we do not know the reason for localisation and further research in this area may well provide clues to aid the combat of an infection.

The symptoms of a disease are not usually caused by the simple mass of cells produced although very large numbers may sometimes occur as in the lungs of a patient infected by pneumonia. More commonly it is the products of the pathogens—*the toxins*—that cause the symptoms. These substances are usually produced extracellularly although in Gram-negative bacteria, the cell-wall lipopolysaccharides are often toxic. Microbial toxins act in extremely small amounts and they are amongst the most lethal compounds known. For example, 1 mg of botulinus toxin is sufficient to kill more than a million guinea pigs. It is evident that a massive infection is not necessarily required to cause death and unfortunately it is also obvious that such toxins pose a potential threat if they are used as the agents of biological warfare. In spite of the importance of toxins we are only recently beginning to gain an insight into their mode of action. Some are enzymes; for example they may lyse red blood cells (the haemolysins) or bind specifically to essential cell components as instanced by the diphtheria toxin which inhibits the transfer of amino acids from RNA to the growing polypeptide chain in protein synthesis.

The growth of the microbial pathogen may result in the death of the host although from the point of view of an efficient parasite in a long-term ecological situation, it is obviously advantageous to set up an equilibrium by which relatively little damage is done to the host which continues to live and release parasites to colonise fresh hosts. For example, a human typhoid carrier may have no recognisable symptoms yet will go on excreting typhoid bacteria for a long period of time and thus pose considerable problems for the epidemiologist concerned in the eradication of the disease.

(3) *Release*. Microorganisms are released from the infected host. This commonly occurs in a particular region which is characteristic of the disease and may or may not be the same as the point of entry and multiplication. In animals, release can occur from the respiratory system as droplets (coughs and sneezes), the alimentary tract usually in the faeces, the urinogenital tract or the skin.

(4) *Spread*. There are many ways by which a microorganism may spread from one host to another. Direct contact may be involved as in venereal disease. Spread may be airborne carried in droplets, dust or spores as in most respiratory

97

infections or in fungal diseases of plants. Many intestinal infections are water-borne or are spread by infected food. Alternatively a carrier such as an insect may be concerned. The mode used will depend partly on the ability of the microorganism to survive outside the host. An example of a restricted survival time can be seen in the bacterium causing the venereal disease of syphilis. At the other extreme are sporing organisms; the island of Gruinard off the Scottish coast was experimentally infected with anthrax spores in 1943 and it is still too dangerous to land there without special precautions. The spread of infection may involve a further multiplication; for example in food or in an insect vector. Indeed, in some organisms the normal means of multiplication is outside the host which becomes infected almost by chance.

In order to eradicate a particular disease we can interfere with any of these four phases in the cycle. Unfortunately it is outside the scope of this volume to deal with all these phases in detail and further discussion must be restricted to events occurring within the host.

### Resistance to infection

The tissues and fluids of animals, to a lesser extent of plants, provide an ideal nutrient environment for microbial growth and such growth can be very rapid if allowed to go on unhindered. How have we and other higher organisms managed to survive and evolve? The reason, of course, lies in our ability to combat infection. Although the means used are strictly speaking a characteristic of the host rather than the microorganism, their study has usually been coupled for historical reasons with that of microbiology. Resistance to infection can take two forms; it can be of a non-specific type present in hosts not previously exposed to infection—a constitutive resistance, or it can be induced by the presence of a particular microorganism.

(1) *Constitutive resistance.* It has been said that the surface layers of a plant or an animal act as a primary barrier to microbial invasion. However, if entry is effected, then there are a variety of defences open to the host. Non-specific antimicrobial agents may be produced; one of these is the enzyme lysozyme (see p. 13) present in natural secretions and extracts of animal organs, while plants often produce phenolic antimicrobial agents. However, the most impor-tant constitutive defence mechanism in animals is *phagocytosis*. A whole series of different types of phagocytes present a defence in depth starting with the macrophages at the primary focus of infection, continuing with the polymorpho-nuclear leucocytes attracted to the regional lymph nodes by the inflammatory response to the white blood cells and ending with the reticuloendothelial system. Phagocytosis is normally followed by the lysis of the engulfed cells. However, a few microbes are able to avoid this fate; some are resistant to phagocytosis (e.g. the capsulate pneumococcus discussed on p. 83); some are engulfed but are unaffected by the lytic enzymes of the phagocyte and may, as in the case of the tubercle bacillus, actually grow intracellularly; some produce substances called

98

leucocidins which kill the phagocytes. A quite different defence mechanism occurs against virus attack; infected cells produce a protein called *interferon* which prevents further viral attack in a non-specific manner.

It is evident that there are various levels of defence and that microorganisms differ in their ability to overcome them—a measure of their pathogenicity and virulence.

(2) *Inducible resistance—immunology*. In higher animals there is a secondary defence against infection should a particular organism succeed in establishing itself. The microorganism induces the formation of specific proteins called *antibodies* which combine with them and render them more susceptible to lysis or phagocytosis. This production of specific antibodies is part of a general phenomenon by which animals react to the presence of foreign substances called *antigens* and it is not unlike the stimulation of induced enzymes by the inducer. The study of the immune response is called immunology and it is of considerable importance both to medicine and to biology in general. Let us consider the nature of antigens and antibodies and the consequences of the reaction between them.

*Antigens*. All sorts of substances are capable of inducing the synthesis of specific antibodies—in other words are capable of acting as antigens. In general they have to be high molecular weight polymers such as proteins and polysaccharides. On the surface of such macromolecules there are particular regions called *antigenic-determinant groups* that react with antibodies; a protein molecule may have as many as a hundred of such groupings corresponding to particular arrangements of amino acids. On the other hand, low-molecular weight substances are not normally antigenic although they may become determinant groups when combined into a large molecule. The most important characteristic of this antigenic capacity is in the specificity of the antibody produced. Protein molecules that differ only in one or two amino acids along the chain or chains can be distinguished. Indeed, the specificity is similar to that between an enzyme and a substrate and implies a non-covalent linkage between the antibody and the antigen which depends upon a close approximation of complementary surfaces akin to a lock and key.

*Antibodies*. Antibodies are proteins occurring in the globulin fraction of serum. Since virtually every protein and many polysaccharides injected into an animal can evoke the formation of a unique antibody and since many substances that have only been produced artificially in the laboratory can be made to act as antigenic-determinant groups, a very large number of different antibodies can potentially be produced by a single animal, a number that has been estimated as being at least $10^6$. The antibody molecules are made up of two specific regions joined by a non-specific region shared by a whole group of antibodies. The specific regions are the ones which actually combine with the antigen so that the antibody behaves as a divalent molecule, an important characteristic in the formation of precipitates or in agglutination.

One of the most puzzling aspects of immunology concerns the capability of animals to produce such a wide range of different protein molecules, albeit with

certain structural similarities. One theory supposes that there are a corresponding number of structural genes each coding for a particular antibody molecule;
the entry of the antigen in some way induces the formation of its appropriate
antigen. A more likely hypothesis, according to present evidence, is that there
are only relatively few structural genes involved but these are highly mutable
to give the variety of antibodies we find in practice. It is assumed that as a
result of this plasticity there is a range of specific-antibody forming cells called
plasma cells; the presence of a particular antigen triggers off multiplication of
the corresponding plasma cells and hence leads to the production of the appropriate antibody. Among other things, this theory explains the fact that once we

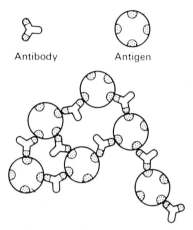

Antibody       Antigen

Antigen-antibody complex

**Figure 8.4**   The formation of a precipitate between a divalent antibody
and a quadrivalent antigen (the com-
bining sites are represented by shaded
areas). The lattice must be considered
as growing indefinitely in three
dimensions

have been exposed to a particular infection, we gain a specific immunity since
there will remain an excess of the specific antibody-forming cells.

*The antibody-antigen reaction.* The basic reaction is a combination of specific regions of the antibody with the appropriate determinant groups on the
antigen. Since the antibody is divalent and the antigen is normally multivalent,
such a reaction leads to the formation of a lattice-like multimolecular complex
(Fig. 8.4). If the antigen is soluble, precipitation will result.

Let us consider what will happen when an animal is infected with a microorganism to which it has not been previously exposed. The microorganisms are
phagocytosed and their components eventually find their way to the lymphoid
tissues where antibodies are produced against them. However, we have seen
that a microorganism will contain about a thousand different protein molecules,

100

let alone polysaccharides and other potential antigens. In theory, antibodies will be formed against all of them although in practice surface antigens are much the most important. The polymers of the cell wall, the capsule, fimbriae and flagella, occur on the outer surface of the cell and are usually present in large amounts compared with other antigens. We can consider the cell as one vast macromolecular antigen with the determinant groups on these surface polymers. Reaction with the appropriate antibody leads to a cross-linked lattice resulting in precipitation or, as it is called *agglutination* of the cells. In the body, such a combination with antibody leads to a much increased susceptibility to the host defence mechanisms leading to lysis and phagocytosis.

The most important use of immunology to the microbiologist lies in its provision of a means of identification by the use of an appropriate specific antibody. For example, we have seen that there are over a hundred types of pneumococci which vary in the chemical nature of the capsular polysaccharide and we can distinguish between them by testing the ability of specific antibody preparations to agglutinate our unknown pneumococcal suspension. Such testing is of particular value to the epidemiologist trying to trace the spread of an infection as it enables him to 'fingerprint' a specific type and study its distribution and movement.

## ANTIMICROBIAL AGENTS AND CHEMOTHERAPY

As soon as it was realised that disease could be caused by microorganisms, attempts were made to produce chemicals which killed them or at least prevented their growth and so the search for antimicrobial agents was initiated. At first cheap substances which killed as many microbes as possible and could be used for chemical sterilisation were sought. The most effective compounds were substances like chlorine, hypochlorites, phenol, salts of heavy metals and detergents. Those agents called *disinfectants* were used on inanimate objects or, in treatment of water, at low concentrations so that possible toxicity to higher organisms was not important. Indeed, most of the chemicals were general protoplasmic poisons acting, for example, by denaturing proteins. Soon people became concerned with the possibility of producing substances which could also be used in contact with higher organisms and, in particular, with man. *Antiseptics* were required for skin disinfection or in the treatment of small wounds while *chemotherapeutic agents* were designed to act on already established infections by absorption into the circulating fluids. For this purpose substances were required which had a specific inhibitory effect against microorganisms—that is, had a *selective toxicity*. None of the substances commonly used as disinfectants had this property since unfortunately higher organisms are generally much more susceptible to chemicals than are microorganisms and, in particular, are bacteria and viruses. Although Lister had introduced the use of phenol in his 'aseptic' surgery and although many of the results were beneficial, the introduction of phenol into open wounds was almost certainly harmful since it inhibited the host defence mechanisms as a result of its selective toxicity towards animal cells compared with microorganisms. A selective

101

toxicity to microorganisms was required but how could such substances be discovered? In the early years of this century the search for such an agent was essentially a 'hit and miss' affair involving the testing of a wide variety of synthetic organic compounds. A few substances of marginal value were obtained, but no real progress was made until the discovery of the sulphonamides, a group of chemicals based on the structure of sulphanilamide. Although the sulphonamides were and still are used against certain bacterial infections of animals and men, their discovery initiated a more general search for agents with selective toxicity. The reason for this arose from the finding that their inhibitory effect against sensitive bacteria could be overcome by adding $p$ aminobenzoic acid. Closer study showed that the sulphonamides acted by competing with $p$ aminobenzoic acid for the active site of an enzyme converting the latter to folic acid, an essential coenzyme for a variety of metabolic conversions.

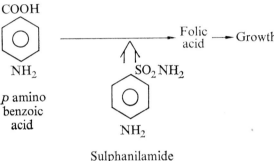

Sulphanilamide

This competitive inhibition was due to the similar structure of sulphanilamide and $p$ aminobenzoic acid, a general phenomenon well recognised in biochemistry. This discovery led to great excitement since it opened up the possibility of a systematic production of chemotherapeutic agents by synthesising analogues of microbial metabolites other than $p$ aminobenzoic acid.

Microbial
metabolite ———→ Growth
Analogue of microbial
metabolite

Since then a very large number of such analogues have been produced, many of which inhibit microbial growth. However, most of the compounds are toxic to higher organisms for the simple reason that most microbial metabolites are common to the cellular forms of life because of the unity of biochemistry referred to previously. Substances and reactions must be found which are specific to microorganisms and inhibitors produced against them. However, this approach has unfortunately still not led to the production of any really useful chemotherapeutic agents, but the reason may lie partly in lack of knowledge of

102

the more sophisticated mechanisms involved in the growth and metabolism of microorganisms.

Before long a new approach began to dominate chemotherapy stemming from the discovery that microorganisms can themselves produce antimicrobial agents called *antibiotics*. This phenomenon had been known since the early days of microbiology and Fleming in 1929 had described an antibiotic produced by the fungus *Penicillium notatum* which he called penicillin and which seemed to have many of the properties required for an ideal chemotherapeutic agent (see Fig. 8.5). However, little progress was made in its purification. In those days chemists knew little microbiology, microbiologists knew little chemistry, there was little understanding between the two and biochemistry was in its infancy. So the project languished until the early 1940's when methods

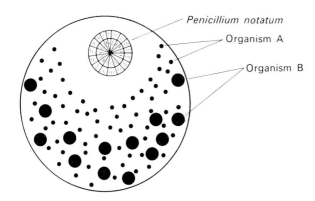

Penicillium notatum
Organism A
Organism B

**Figure 8.5** The results of an experiment similar to that by which Fleming originally discovered penicillin. A plate is seeded over the whole surface with two organisms, one producing small colonies (A) and one producing large colonies (B). Penicillin diffuses from the colony of *Penicillium notatum* and inhibits organism B at a lower concentration than organism A.

were finally perfected for the purification and it became clear that penicillin was a far more effective chemotherapeutic agent than anything that had been previously discovered. Suddenly it was realised that antibiotic-producing microbes were not uncommon, particularly in soil where they are thought to prevent the growth of competitors. Microbiologists came back from their holidays weighed down with soil samples and with the gleam of Nobel Prizes in their eyes. A large range of antibiotics were discovered and chemotherapy was revolutionised to the extent that most infections caused by cellular microorganisms could be treated. What, then, is the basis of the selective toxicity of these antibiotics? This is not just an academic question since more and more microorganisms are developing resistance to the substances in use today (see p. 88) and it is likely that we have already exhausted the range of antibiotics occurring in nature. A knowledge of the mode of action of successful antibiotics should provide clues to the design of new and possibly better chemotherapeutic agents. Such a knowledge is slowly becoming available—slowly because it requires a detailed understanding of microbial physiology. For example, in spite of a vast number of papers published on the mode of action of penicillin, it is only recently that the site has been pinned down as an inhibition of the final stage of the biosynthesis of the peptidoglycan of the prokaryotic cell wall. At once the selective toxicity of penicillin was explained since eukaryotes like ourselves have no structures resembling the mucopeptide.

Although selective agents against cellular microorganisms and, in particular, against prokaryotes, are now available, the same is not true for agents against viruses. Unfortunately, the multiplication of the virus is entirely dependant on the host cell and any attempt to inhibit this multiplication almost inevitably results in the destruction of the host cell as well. Although there are possibilities in preventing the virus attacking and entering a cell, it is probable that the development of chemotherapeutic agents against virus infections and against cancer will require a much more sophisticated understanding of the working of a cell than we have at present.

## MICROBIOLOGICAL CONTROL

In general parasitic microorganisms do harm to man, either by causing disease directly or by affecting animals and crops. However, they can also be useful by eliminating or preventing the spread of pests. Consider myxomatosis, a virus disease of rabbits. The disease occurred in the western hemisphere and rabbits were generally resistant to it in such areas. In 1953 the disease was introduced to Europe and later into Australia where it had been absent. There was a catastrophic epidemic amongst the sensitive rabbit population which was almost wiped out. Agricultural land became available which had previously been ravaged and although there has been a later tendency for resistant rabbits and less virulent viruses to develop, the potentiality of such microbiological control is obvious. In particular, there has been much interest in the eradication of insect pests by this method, an attractive idea since it is not associated with the pollution dangers that attend the use of chemical insecticides.

# 9 The ecology of microorganisms and their value to man

Microorganisms make up a significant percentage of the total biomass on the earth. Indeed, as a result of their high rate of growth, their metabolic activity and their adaptability they are of even more importance in the proper functioning of ecosystems than their total mass would indicate. This chapter will be concerned with some of their most important roles in maintaining an environment on the earth suitable for life and living as we now understand it. In addition, the ways in which some of these activities have been harnessed for the benefit of man will be considered.

## CYCLES OF ELEMENTS AND MATTER

We have seen that the main elements from which living organisms are made up are C, H, O, N, S and P. Growth, considered over the whole range of living organisms on earth, consists in the conversion of these elements present in an inorganic form to the organic compounds that make up living matter. The energy for this conversion is ultimately derived from solar sources by photosynthesis.

$$\underset{\text{Solar energy}}{\text{Inorganic forms of elements} \xrightarrow{\hspace{3cm}} \text{Organic forms of elements}}$$

If this was the only process occurring, life would soon cease as the inorganic forms of the elements and, in particular, of C and N were bound up into organic matter. In fact, the reverse process called *mineralisation* must also occur and is brought about by the activity of living organisms so that cycles of elements or of matter occur.

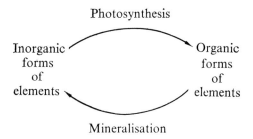

If this was the only process occurring, life would soon cease as the inorganic forms of the elements and, in particular, of C and N were bound up into organic matter. In fact, the reverse process called *mineralisation* must also occur and is brought about by the activity of living organisms so that cycles of elements or of matter occur.

The situation is complicated by the existence in nature of oxidised and reduced states of most of the essential elements; organisms may only be able to use one or other form and further cycles therefore exist between them.

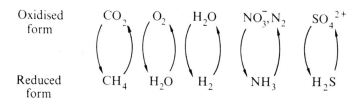

| Oxidised form | $CO_2$ | $O_2$ | $H_2O$ | $NO_3^-, N_2$ | $SO_4^{2+}$ |
|---|---|---|---|---|---|
| Reduced form | $CH_4$ | $H_2O$ | $H_2$ | $NH_3$ | $H_2S$ |

Let us consider in more detail the way in which carbon undergoes cyclic changes.

**The carbon cycle**

The major inorganic source of carbon for the growth of living organisms is carbon dioxide either in the atmosphere or in solution in surface waters. It is converted to an organic form by the action of autotrophic organisms which can use it as a sole source of carbon. The most important autotrophs in this process are those carrying out an oxygen-producing type of photosynthesis—the seed plants on land and the algae in water. Photosynthetic and chemosynthetic autotrophic bacteria also play a role, though a relatively minor one.

$$CO_2 \xrightarrow[\text{Autotrophs}]{} \text{Organic C}$$

A small part of the inorganic C will be in the reduced form of methane which can be utilised as the sole source of carbon and energy by a special group of aerobic bacteria which convert it into organic carbon and $CO_2$.

$$CH_4 \xrightarrow[\substack{\text{Methane-utilising} \\ \text{bacteria}}]{CO_2} \text{Organic C}$$

The rate of conversion of inorganic to organic C is such that in 20–30 years the total $CO_2$ in the atmosphere would be completely exhausted in the absence of replenishment from the oceans. However, the reverse process of the mineralisation of organic to inorganic C by the action of heterotrophs will prevent this exhaustion; the major end-product is $CO_2$ but some bacteria will produce $CH_4$ by anaerobic respiration and fermentation (p. 62).

$$\text{Organic C} \xrightarrow[\text{Heterotrophs}]{(CH_4)} CO_2$$

So a carbon cycle is built up to give an equilibrium situation with equal rates in both directions.

106

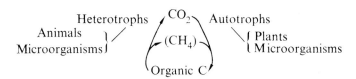

Although the conversion of inorganic to organic C by the plant kingdom and by autotrophic microorganisms is relatively straightforward, the reverse process by the animal kingdom and heterotrophic microorganisms is more complex and must be considered in greater detail.

*The Mineralisation of organic carbon.* Heterotrophic organisms, be they animals or microbes, obtain their carbon and energy by the metabolism of an organic source provided by another form of life.

$$\text{Organic C} \xrightarrow{\text{Heterotroph}} \text{Organic C} \begin{pmatrix} \text{Cells and} \\ \text{organic} \\ \text{end-products} \end{pmatrix}$$
$$\searrow$$
$$CO_2(CH_4)$$

As a result, some of the organic C is mineralised while the rest is converted to further organic C in the form of new growth of the heterotroph or as end-products of metabolism. The efficiency of this conversion will vary according to the organism and to the aerobic or anaerobic nature of the process. The particular heterotroph and any organic C it may produce then acts as the food source for other heterotrophs and so on along a food chain. At each stage of this food chain a percentage of the original organic C is mineralised until the process is complete.

$$\overset{CO_2(CH_4)}{\text{Autotrophic}} \overset{\uparrow}{\underset{\text{Heterotroph}}{\text{organic C}}} \rightarrow \text{organic C} \overset{CO_2(CH_4)}{\underset{\text{Heterotroph}}{\uparrow}} \rightarrow \begin{pmatrix} CO_2(CH_4) \\ \text{organic C} \overset{\uparrow}{\underset{\text{Heterotroph}}{}} \rightarrow \end{pmatrix}_n$$

Microorganisms play an exceedingly important part in this process. Any compound which is a component of a living organism must be susceptible to mineralisation or it would eventually accumulate on the surface of the earth so that ultimately all the carbon would be in this unavailable form. We have seen that microorganisms as a whole have a very wide ability to break down organic compounds and they can in fact metabolise all naturally-occurring chemicals. It is a matter of common observation that dead animal or plant material falling on soil or in water is fairly rapidly destroyed. This occurs by the sequential action of a variety of microorganisms, each utilising one or more component compounds. If any substance accumulates, then the growth of a microbe capable of utilising it is favoured. However, some plant components in soil are used only slowly and some of them together with the products of

107

saprophytic microbes constitute the humus, a complex mixture of materials which helps to maintain a suitable texture for plant growth.

The whole subject of the ecology of soil microorganisms is a very complex one and we have little real understanding of the interactions occurring. The problem is made worse by the presence of microenvironments in the soil where the conditions may be quite different from those occurring more generally. For example, microbes can be adsorbed onto the surface of soils or food particles and it is exceedingly difficult to mimic these conditions in the laboratory.

An important factor affecting the rate and extent of mineralisation is the availability of oxygen. If conditions become anaerobic as may occur in a waterlogged soil, then the accumulation of acids and other inhibitory end-products of fermentation prevents further microbial growth and metabolism. In this way, layers of partly decomposed plant material can accumulate as in peat deposits. Such a phenomenon of partial attack is made use of in *silage* production. Suitable plant material such as grasses is packed into cylindrical towers or pits called silos, where the conditions rapidly become anaerobic. Carbohydrate fermentation by bacteria leads to the production of lactic acid which accumulates. The pH falls and quickly a stable situation is reached in which the silage can be stored for long periods prior to its use as an animal fodder.

The action of microorganisms, then, is of fundamental importance in maintaining the carbon cycle and all naturally-occurring organic compounds are eventually mineralised to $CO_2$ and $CH_4$. However, man is introducing increasingly large amounts of synthetic organic compounds into the environment particularly as herbicides and pesticides. Many are not subject to microbial attack and therefore accumulate. In most cases we do not know what will be the effect of this accumulation and, apart from any direct toxicity to man we cannot usually assess how far normal food chains will be broken with equally disastrous results. Clearly if such chemicals must be used, care should be taken to ensure that they are non-toxic to man, but they should also be designed to be eventually subject to microbial mineralisation—in other words they should be *biodegradable*, if only slowly. An example of what can be done can be seen in the case of synthetic detergents. In the early days of their commercial production, such detergents were not biodegradable and caused considerable problems as a result of their accumulation, particularly in streams and rivers where layers of foam built up. Legislation led to the design of detergents which are subject to microbial attack and the problem was apparently solved. However, a further problem has arisen. Most detergents contain phosphate; microbial attack liberates inorganic phosphate which may itself cause pollution problems by eutrophication (p. 110); the next stage must be to design biodegradable compounds which do not contain phosphate.

An interesting question arising from the contamination of our environment with unnatural chemicals is how far can mutation affect enzymes causing a change in their substrate-specificity so as to allow quite different and new compounds to be attacked? In other words, how far can pollution bring about evolutionary changes resulting in the overcoming of the source of the pollution? Certainly we can show this process in the laboratory provided that the new substrate is sufficiently close in structure to a normal substrate. However, the evolution of microbes attacking compounds like polyvinyl chloride or nylon may be more prolonged, if it occurs at all.

*Sewage treatment.* The development of big cities has resulted in the production of large amounts of organic wastes in a restricted area. If the untreated

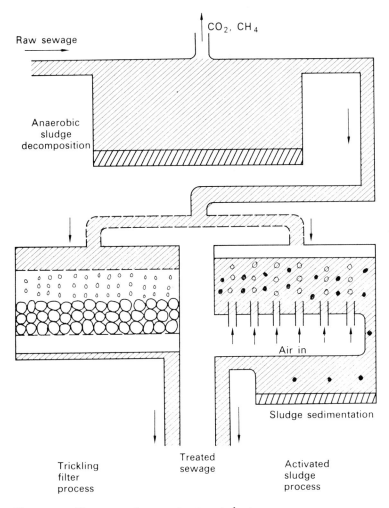

**Figure 9.1** Two types of sewage treatment plants

sewage is simply discharged into near-by waters as is all too common, two problems may result. Firstly, there is a public health hazard caused by contamination with potentially pathogenic microorganisms. Secondly, the affected waters may be made anaerobic by the action of microbial aerobic metabolism on the dissolved organic compounds; animal life is destroyed by the resultant lack of oxygen. Consequently some treatment of raw sewage is desirable to decrease the level of organic compounds. Since this is essentially a process of mineralisation, the ability of microorganisms to carry it out is used in the design of sewage-treatment plants. There are two basic stages involved in such plants.

(1) *Sedimentation and anaerobic decomposition.* The solid particles in raw sewage are allowed to sediment in large settling tanks. The precipitate undergoes an anaerobic decomposition with the production of $CO_2$ and $CH_4$ and the undigested material is removed periodically from the bottom of the tank.

(2) *Aerobic decomposition of soluble fraction.* The soluble matter in sewage is subject to aerobic microbial decomposition. This may be brought about by a trickling filter in which the liquid sewage is sprayed onto the surface of a bed of crushed stone impregnated with mineralising microbes. Another method is based on the fact that if air is passed through liquid sewage, a precipitate is formed which becomes rich in microorganisms. This precipitate or activated sludge as it is charmingly called, can be added to further aerated soluble sewage and will cause a rapid mineralisation. The processes are represented in Fig. 9.1.

A further problem can still occur. The growth of algae in rivers or lakes is often limited by the level of minerals and, in particular, by nitrates, phosphate and sulphate. Various factors are leading to a much increased rate of addition of such nutrients to inland waters. This process of enrichment is called *eutrophication* and it can be caused by various types of pollution such as the addition of treated sewage or of industrial waste or by drainage from agricultural land which is being increasingly intensively farmed. The result of this eutrophication is initially seen in the formation of rich algal blooms visible to the naked eye. The organisms responsible for such blooms are frequently planktonic blue-green algae (Plate 9.1, facing p. 110), particularly those which possess gas vacuoles giving them sufficient buoyancy to stay in the well-lit surface layers. Unfortunately such algal blooms can directly or indirectly lead to a marked deterioration in the quality of inland waters and can present serious economic problems by virtue of the water containing substances toxic to fish or of difficulties in filtration. Further, when the algae die, the decomposition of their cells by bacteria may lead to anaerobic conditions which, if extended through the body of water, may lead to the death of fish and other animals.

### The nitrogen cycle

In nature a suitable source of nitrogen is often the factor limiting growth in an ecosystem. Although there is a plentiful supply of molecular nitrogen in the atmosphere, we have seen that there are only a restricted group of nitrogen-fixing microorganisms capable of using it. It is, therefore, imperative that there should be an efficient cyclisation between organic and inorganic nitrogen. Inorganic nitrogen in the form of ammonia or nitrate is converted to an organic state mainly by the action of plants and microorganisms while if nitrate is used it must be first reduced to ammonia. We have already discussed the differences between microorganisms in the ability to synthesise their amino acids, purines,

110

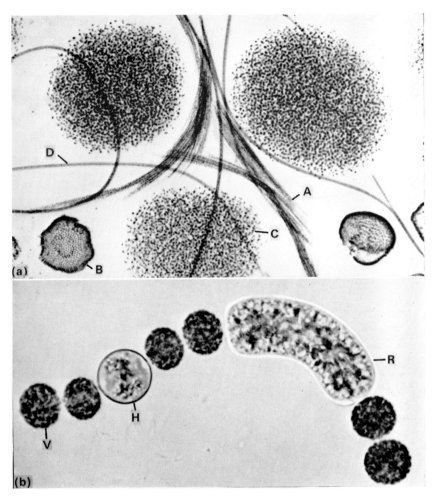

**Plate 9.1** (a) Planktonic blue-green algae from Esthwaite Water, English Lake District. A, *Aphanizomenon;* B, *Gomphosphaeria;* C, *Microcystis;* D,*Oscillatoria.* ×135

(b) Part of a thread of the blue-green alga *Anabaena.* V, vegetative cell with gas vacuoles; H, heterocyst; R, young resting spore (akinete). ×1350 (Photographs kindly supplied by Hilda Canter-Lund.)

pyrimidines and other organic nitrogenous compounds for themselves and therefore in their ability to use an inorganic source of nitrogen. The responsibility for the mineralisation of this organic nitrogen to ammonia lies largely with microorganisms either by their action on dead organisms or by their degradation of animal excretory products. In aerobic soils, nitrifying bacteria may oxidise the ammonia to nitrate (p. 65), a process which may be harmful to agriculture since although nitrate may be better utilised than ammonia for plant growth, it is more readily leached from the ground. Further, if conditions become anaerobic, denitrification occurs by the anaerobic respiration of certain bacteria (p. 63) and this results in the liberation of molecular

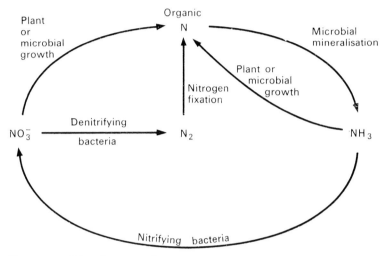

**Figure 9.2**   The nitrogen cycle

nitrogen, the loss that can only be made up by nitrogen-fixing microorganisms or by the addition of fertilisers. Clearly microorganisms can influence the availability of nitrogen in agriculture in many ways.

The nitrogen cycle is summarised in Fig. 9.2.

## THE INDUSTRIAL PRODUCTION OF MICROORGANISMS AND THEIR PRODUCTS

The industrial growth of microorganisms can be designed either to produce the microbial cells themselves or their products. Let us consider these aims in turn.

### Microbial foods

Microorganisms theoretically provide an excellent source of food for animal and human nutrition. They have a high content of protein, essential amino acids and vitamins. Although the full potential of microbial foods has only been realised recently, microorganisms have often been used to ferment, preserve and sometimes enrich animal or plant foods which would otherwise rapidly

111

decay. This has been particularly true in dairy products such as in the manufacture of butter, yoghurt and cheese from milk. Let us consider cheese production. Milk proteins and fat are first precipitated as a solid curd which is then subjected to a microbial ripening process. The end-product of this ripening, and therefore the type of cheese produced, is largely determined by the process used (heating, pressing, salting etc.) and by the microorganisms concerned. In the common so-called 'Cheddar' cheese the responsible organisms are the lactic acid bacteria already present in the curd; their growth and subsequent death and lysis liberate proteolytic and lipolytic enzymes which give the cheese its characteristic flavour, or, as some would have it, lack of flavour. In other cheeses a specific microbial culture is introduced; propionibacteria with their production of propionic acid and $CO_2$ give many Swiss cheeses their flavour and holes while fungi are used for 'blue' cheeses.

However, dairy products are expensive and add little to the nutrient value of the original milk. A more useful approach is to enrich traditional carbohydrate foods by the growth of microorganisms although care must then be taken to avoid contamination by potentially dangerous pathogens. Much interest has also been shown recently in the large-scale growth of food microbes as a means to alleviate the world food shortage. Clearly the nutrients for microbial growth must be very cheap to make the process worthwhile. Three main approaches have been made to the problem, all of them sufficiently recent to leave the eventual pattern of their development uncertain.

(1) *Photosynthetic microorganisms.* Although photosynthetic organisms do not require the addition of expensive organic nutrients, they do require light and so far no economical process has been developed.

(2) *Heterotrophic organisms.* If heterotrophs are to be used, it is essential to grow them on a carbon and energy source which is cheap, easily available and reproducible in content. One possibility is to use carbohydrate wastes from industrial processes such as molasses from sugar production, sawdust from wood production and sulphite–waste liquor from paper production. Microorganisms are grown aerobically on these materials or their hydrolysis products. Another method is to use fossil fuels as carbon and energy sources. Heterotrophic microorganisms can grow on the straight-chain hydrocarbons present in oil or natural gas, both cheap and readily available substrates, at least until the world's reserves run out. The products of growth are microbial cells and carbon dioxide and as much as 80% of the hydrocarbon may be converted to biomass of which about 50% may be protein. A large-scale industrial process for producing food yeast from oil by continuous culture has been developed and the product represents one of the cheapest forms of protein available competitive in price to soyabean meal and fishmeal. The yeast has been fed on a large scale to animals like poultry and pigs with no signs of toxic effects. Since it is tasteless, there seems no reason why it shouldn't be used for human food provided a suitable flavour and texture can be incorporated. Such a microbial food should have a considerable impact on the world

food situation as can be seen from the calculation that 10% of the present world annual oil production could provide the protein requirement for the whole of the human population. Such calculations highlight the foolishness of a too-rapid and intemperate burning of the world's reserves of fossil fuels to provide heat and power. Methane in the form of natural gas provides another cheap carbon and energy source although the ability to use it for growth is restricted to bacteria and we know little of their use as animal or human food-stuffs.

(3) *Chemoautotrophic bacteria.* The use of these organisms has partly been a by-product of the question—how can we best employ electrical power to produce organic nutrients? This problem has concerned those en-gaged in research into space travel although it has implications for future times when electrical power is much cheaper than at present and, at the same time, fossil fuels are largely exhausted. One method is to convert the electrical power

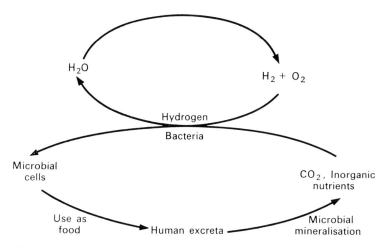

**Figure 9.3** A scheme for the continuous production of microbial food using electrical energy

to light which is used to grow photosynthetic microorganisms. Another possi-bility is to use hydrogen and oxygen to produce water, a reaction which can then be reversed by electrolysis. In prolonged space travel the excreta produced by the astronauts would be mineralised by microorganisms and the inorganic products would then be used as the nutrients for the growth of hydrogen bacteria which would then be fed back to the astronauts. The cycle is sum-marised in Fig. 9.3. It might seem that such a regime would not be exactly a gourmet's dream, but it cannot be doubted that men will always be found to put up with such discomforts to aid space exploration.

## Microbial products

In theory, the formation of any microbial metabolite can be made the basis of a commercial process. However, apart from the industrial need for the product, the most important question has always been the relative cost of a biological process compared with a chemical synthesis. In the past most systems have been concerned with the production of relatively simple extracellular end-products of metabolism which usually occur in large quantities. Most of these substances were produced anaerobically by microbial fermentation and hence the industry that grew up was known as the fermentation industry. Unfortunately, however, the term has tended to be applied to other more recent developments where growth is essentially aerobic such as the production of food yeasts from hydrocarbons mentioned previously. Let us consider some of the most important industrial products of microorganisms in the past, the present and the likely future.

(1) *Alcohol production.* Historically the most important microbial product has been ethanol, formed by yeast as a result of carbohydrate fermentation (p. 64). The simplest methods involve the use of a plant material with a high sugar content such as grapes as a substrate to be fermented directly to produce wine; the type of wine will depend on the grape and on the variety of yeast. The process consists in crushing the grapes to a clear grape juice which is fermented either by yeasts present naturally on the grapes or by the addition of pure 'starter' cultures of appropriate wine yeasts. The fermentation is almost entirely an alcoholic one since the growth of contaminating bacteria is prevented by the high acidity and sugar content of the grape juice. After fermentation is complete or has reached a required stage, the yeast is removed and the wine is allowed to age by a non-microbiological process. Care must be taken to prevent microbial spoilage, particularly by the action of bacteria oxidising ethanol to acetic acid which will occur if the conditions become too aerobic in the ageing process; if such an oxidation occurs, vinegar is the ultimate product.

In beer production, the carbohydrate fermented is the starch present in barley, corn or rice. Since alcohol-producing yeasts are unable to break down starch themselves, a preliminary depolymerisation stage is required. For this purpose, use can be made either of the starch-hydrolysing amylases present in barley as occurs in European beer production or of fungal amylases which are added in Japanese sake production. Following this initial depolymerisation, special brewers' yeasts produce the ethanol. Different types of beer are made by using different yeasts, by the addition of hops or by the presence of a later, low-temperature secondary fermentation in lager production. Most beer manufacture still depends upon a batch fermentation in large vats; continuous culture would be much more efficient but the inherent conservatism of the brewers and their customers has slowed down its introduction in most countries.

There are two further uses of the yeast alcoholic fermentation. One is in industrial ethanol production although the more competitive chemical synthesis of ethanol is displacing microbial fermentation. The other process is in breadmaking where the leavening stage is due to a yeast fermentation producing $CO_2$.

(2) *Other chemical compounds.* The ability of microorganisms to synthesise a wide variety of fermentation end-products has been made the basis of what was a highly developed fermentation industry. Substances such as glycerol, lactic acid, butylene glycol, acetone, butanol, acetic acid and butyric acid have been made in this way. However, rises in the costs of suitable carbohydrates as raw materials and the development of more efficient chemical syntheses have made the microbial methods increasingly uneconomic. With the exception of alcoholic drinks and bread making, the fermentation industry was in danger of extinction when the discovery of the chemotherapeutic use of antibiotics in the 1940's led to a rebirth. Most antibiotics are very complex chemical substances and although methods may be available for their chemical synthesis, microbial production is usually much cheaper. Research has led to the introduction of more efficient antibiotic-producing strains which are jealously guarded by the responsible industry. For example, the strains of *Penicillium* in current industrial use produce as much as a thousand times as much penicillin per unit volume of fermentation liquor than did the original strain of *Penicillium notatum* isolated by Fleming. Again, batch culture has been employed for antibiotic production although for a different reason from that in the brewing industry. Antibiotics are usually only synthesised when active growth is over at the end of the exponential phase. Substances like antibiotics which are not normal products of active growth are known as *secondary metabolites.* Their function is far from clear. It has been supposed that the capacity for antibiotic production is an advantage in the struggle for existence and it is true that nearly all antibiotics are synthesised by organisms which normally live in the soil—a highly competitive environment where the ability to kill other microbes would be valuable. However, the hypothesis is unproved and it remains an enigma why a restricted microbial group like the actinomycetes are capable of producing such an enormous range of exotic chemicals some of which appear to have no antibiotic activity.

The commercial production of antibiotics, then, acted as a stimulus to the microbial fermentation industry and another more recent stimulus has been the interest in microbial foods mentioned previously. Unfortunately the biological industry as a whole tends to be dominated by non-biologists and the impact of recent discoveries in microbiology and, in particular, in molecular biology have yet to make themselves felt in more applied fields. It has become possible to 'tailor make' microorganisms with the capacity of over-producing almost any microbial metabolite such as a vitamin. Indeed, antibiotic production is an illustration of what can be done, albeit in a rather empirical way. The genetics of microorganisms allow considerable sophistication in the methods used. For example, there is much interest in the commercial production of enzymes. Mutants can be obtained in which the synthesis of the required enzyme is no longer repressed and multiple copies of structural genes can be introduced. Soon 'genetic engineering' in microorganisms may become a reality and we may be able to introduce genes into an organism from a quite unrelated source.

# Conclusion

These last two chapters have been concerned with the more applied aspects of microbiology. Their separation from the more basic or 'pure' aspects is one of convenience and should not imply that the two are indeed separate. As microbiology evolves, the distinction becomes more blurred and is slowly leading to the breakdown of prejudices that caused the 'pure' microbiologist to look down on his applied colleagues as being earthy and uninspired while the latter looked on the former as being ineffectual, effete and superior-minded. At a research level a good general knowledge of microbiology is required for any type of work and in many ways the problems of applied microbiology present the greatest challenges. Research is moving away from a dominant study of a single organism and from the recent era in which many non-microbiologists and, more sadly, some microbiologists grouped microorganisms into two classes— *Escherichia coli* and contaminants. Microbiologists are beginning to realise again the vast and fascinating array of microorganisms. The study of microbial ecology has received a boost from the realisation of the increasing pollution of our planet. At the same time, the immense increase in our knowledge of the biochemistry, genetics and molecular biology of a few organisms is beginning to make itself felt in the more applied fields. In short, microbiology is both an important and a developing subject.

# Additional reading

More detailed reading lists are given in the later volumes of this series to which the reader is referred. In addition, the following more general references may be of value.

BROCK T. D. (1961) *Milestones in Microbiology*. New Jersey: Prentice Hall.
BROCK T. D. (1970) *Biology of Microorganisms*. New Jersey: Prentice Hall.
POSTGATE J. (1969) *Microbes and Man*. Harmondsworth: Penguin Books.
STANIER R. Y., DOUDOROFF M., ADELBERG E. A. (1971) *General Microbiology*. London: Macmillan.

The Symposia of the Society for General Microbiology published yearly by the Cambridge University Press also have many articles of general interest.

# Index